S0-BDP-550

IO·BAPT·PIRANESIVS
ROBERTVS ADAM·
ARCHITECTI

Catalogues of Architectural Drawings in the Victoria and Albert Museum

Robert ADAM

by Alistair Rowan

Victoria and Albert Museum

Frontispiece
Giovanni Battista Piranesi
'The Artist and Robert Adam'
from Plate V of *Campus Martius*, 1762
dedicated to Adam

Published in 1988
by the Victoria and Albert Museum
London SW7 2RL

ISBN 1 851770 70 4

Designed by Simon Rendall

Printed in England
by Jolly & Barber Ltd, Rugby, Warwickshire

Contents

List of Plates 7
Foreword 9
Acknowledgements 10
Introduction 11
Note to the Reader 26
List of Abbreviations 29

CATALOGUE
Studies and Sketches 31
Academic and antique studies (cat. 1–5)
Theoretical and sketch designs (cat. 6–12)
Picturesque compositions (cat. 13–23)
Late romantic landscapes (cat. 24–27)
Sketch designs for unidentified buildings (cat. 28–31)
Sketch designs of architectural details (cat. 32–37)
Sketch designs for tombs and wall monuments (cat. 38–41)
Unidentified sketch designs by different hands (cat. 42–51)

Identified designs (cat. 52–147) 48
Unidentified designs 100
Architecture (cat. 148–152)
Chimneypiece designs (cat. 153–192)
Furniture and metalwork (cat. 193–197)

Select Bibliography 113
Concordance of Numbers 117
Index 119

This volume bears a double dedication:
in the present day to my wife
ANN MARTHA ROWAN
and in the world of the past
to the memory of
JENNY, BETTY AND PEGGY ADAM
who, looking after their brothers in London,
shared their anxieties, their hopes and their successes.

List of Plates

1 Robert or James Adam. Corinthian capital and entablature. (cat. 1)
2 Robert Adam. Neo-antique column base. (cat. 2)
3 Robert Adam. Design for a royal palace or public building. (cat. 6)
4 Robert Adam. A ruined antique shrine. (cat. 7)
5 Robert Adam. A ruined temple converted for Christian use. (cat. 8)
6 Robert Adam. Design for a public building. (cat. 9)
7 Jacques Louis Clérisseau. View of the Temple of Aesculapius at Spalatro. (cat. 14)
8 Francesco Bartolozzi after J. L. Clérisseau. View of the Temple of Aesculapius, from Robert Adam, *Ruins of the Palace of the Emperor Diocletian at Spalatro*, 1764.
9 Robert Adam. Composition of Roman ruins. (cat. 15)
10 Robert Adam. Classical landscape with a river and temples. (cat. 17)
11 Robert Adam. A castle on a cliff. (cat. 25)
12 Robert Adam. A hill-top castle by a lake. (cat. 26)
13 Robert Adam. Design for a colonnaded bridge. (cat. 28)
14 Robert Adam. Design for a rustic bridge. (cat. 29)
15 Robert Adam. Sketch of a thatched country lodge. (cat. 30)
16 Robert Adam. Design for a rustic building in a park. (cat. 31)
17 Robert Adam. Designs for plasterwork ceiling decorations. (cat. 35)
18 Anonymous. Design for a public lavatory. (cat. 42)
19 Anonymous. Sketch for a garden fort. (cat. 43)
20 Robert Adam. Bowood, plan of the entrance hall ceiling. (cat. 52)
21 Robert Adam. Compton Verney, sectional elevation of the entrance court and hall. (cat. 53)
22 Robert Adam. Croome Court, plan and elevation of park gates. (cat. 55)
23 Robert Adam. Gosford House, elevation of park gate. (cat. 58)
24 Robert Adam. Kedleston Hall, section and elevation of a 'Roman' ruin. (cat. 61)
25 Robert Adam. 38, Berkeley Square, London, elevation of a girandole. (cat. 64)
26 Robert Adam. Deputy Ranger's Lodge, Green Park, London, elevation of gateway. After 1778. (cat. 68)
27 Robert Adam. Hyde Park Corner, London, elevation of a triumphal gateway. Before 1778. (cat. 69)
28 Robert Adam. Hyde Park Corner, London, plan of triumphal gateway. (By courtesy of the trustees of Sir John Soane's Museum.)
29 Robert Adam. 13, Mansfield Street, London, plan of back drawing room ceiling, 1772. (cat. 71)
30 Robert Adam. Lord Holland's house, Piccadilly, London, elevation of screen wall. (cat. 72)
31 Robert Adam. Hendon Manor, elevation of a bridge. (cat. 74)
32 Robert Adam. Osterley Park, ground floor plan of the Palladian scheme, 1761. (cat. 76)
33 Robert Adam. Osterley Park, east elevation of Palladian scheme, 1761. (cat. 77)
34 Robert Adam. Osterley Park, sectional elevation of the Palladian scheme, 1761. (cat. 80)
35 Robert Adam. Osterley Park, elevation of entrance front as built. (cat. 81)
36 Osterley Park from the north east. (National Monuments Record.)
37 Osterley Park, plan as completed 1763–1782. (From A. T. Bolton, *The Architecture of Robert and James Adam*, 1922.)
38 Robert Adam. Osterley Park, plan and elevations of the library. (cat. 84)
39 Robert Adam. Osterley Park, plan of the library ceiling, 1766. (cat. 85)
40 Robert Adam. Osterley Park, elevation of library chimneypiece, 1766. (cat. 87)

41 Robert Adam. Osterley Park, plan and elevations of entrance hall, 1767. (cat. 88)
42 Robert Adam. Osterley Park, plan of entrance hall ceiling, 1767. (cat. 89)
43 Robert Adam. Osterley Park, plan and elevations of the dining room. (cat. 91)
44 Robert Adam. Osterley Park, elevation of drawing room chimneypiece. (cat. 94)
45 Robert Adam. Osterley Park, elevation of drawing room grate and fender. (cat. 95)
46 Robert Adam. Osterley Park, elevation of a pier glass for the drawing room, 1773. (cat. 96)
47 Robert Adam. Osterley Park, plan of the drawing room carpet. (cat. 97)
48 Robert Adam. Osterley Park, plan of the drawing room ceiling. (By courtesy of the Trustees of Sir John Soane's Museum.)
49 Robert Adam. Osterley Park, sketch design for the dressing room walls. (cat. 101)
50 Robert Adam. Osterley Park, plan and elevation of the gate lodges, 1777. (cat. 102)
51 Robert Adam. Osterley Park, plan and elevation of a conservatory. (cat. 103)
52 Robert Adam. Osterley Park, plan of a bridge, 1768. (cat. 105)
53 Robert Adam. Osterley Park, elevation of a bridge, 1768. (cat. 107)
54 Robert Adam. Osterley Park, design for a ruined castle, 1774. (cat. 108)
55 Robert Adam. Syon House, elevation of an entrance lodge. (cat. 110)
56 Robert Adam. Syon House, perspective view of the gallery. (cat. 111)
57 Robert Adam. Mamhead House, ground floor plan of the smaller scheme, 1766. (cat. 117)
58 Robert Adam. Mamhead House, west elevation, 1766. (cat. 128)
59 Robert Adam. Mamhead House, plan of a drawing room ceiling, 1766. (cat. 132)
60 Robert Adam. Mamhead House, plan and elevations of a bedroom, 1766. (cat. 133)
61 Robert Adam. Mamhead House, plan and elevations of a dining room, 1766. (cat. 134)
62 Robert Adam. Mamhead House, plan of dining room ceiling, 1766. (cat. 135)
63 Robert Adam. Mamhead House, plan and elevations of a library, 1766. (cat. 136)
64 Robert Adam. Mamhead House, plan of library ceiling, 1766. (cat. 137)
65 Robert Adam. Mamhead House, record elevation of east front. (By courtesy of the Trustees of Sir John Soane's Museum.)
66 S. Lacey after J. P. Neale. Mamhead House. (Engraving in J. P. Neale, *Views of Seats*, series 1, vol. 4, 1821.)
67 Robert Adam. Mistley Hall, perspective sketch of a reservoir and screen, 1774. (cat. 143)
68 Robert Adam. Tulloch Castle, sketch plan and elevation of a ruined garden tower, 1790. (cat. 144)
69 Robert Adam. Wyreside, elevation of entrance front, c.1790. (cat. 146)
70 Wyreside, entrance front. (Etching and aquatint from *The Lonsdale Magazine*, June 1821, vol. II, No. XVIII.)
71 Robert Adam. Sketch elevation of a caryatid chimneypiece. (cat. 154)
72 Robert Adam. Elevation of a caryatid chimneypiece for the gallery at Harewood House, Yorkshire. Pen and water-colour. (The Metropolitan Museum of art, Harris Brisbane Dick Fund, 1934.)
73 Robert Adam. Elevation of chimneypiece with figures of Apollo and Diana. (cat. 156)
74 Chimneypiece in the Oriental Club, Stratford Place, London.
75 Anonymous. Elevation of an Adamesque chimneypiece. (cat. 178)
76 Robert Adam. Elevation of a girandole. (cat. 194)
77 Anonymous. Elevation of a tripod torchère. (cat. 195)

Foreword

Alistair Rowan's catalogue of the drawings by Robert Adam in the Victoria and Albert Museum was largely written in 1984. Published now, it is the latest in the series of monographs written by specialist scholars with the general intention of bringing the Museum's collections of architectural drawings to the attention of a wider public. The existing literature on the Adams is in fact considerable and, as Professor Rowan shows in this volume, much of the Museum's holding is no more than a part of (perhaps illegitimately separate from) the fine collection of Adam office drawings in the Soane Museum. But the V & A, as a national museum, is the nearest thing the country has to a national museum of architecture, and it is right that Robert Adam should have his place in this series. At Osterley the Museum has responsibility with the National Trust for one of the finest of the Adam's great suburban palaces created for a banker and containing some of Robert Adam's most learned and at the same time most joyously inventive interiors. In a sense, the historical moment of the 1980s is not unlike that of the 1750s, when Robert Adam was measuring the Roman remains and Diocletian's palace on the Adriatic and when Horace Walpole was at work, in a very different but as passionately antiquarian style, at Strawberry Hill. Now there is a similar excitement about the ancient world and about the aspects of the European architectural tradition which twentieth-century doctrine has largely removed from our usage. As in the 1750s many people have begun to investigate and to examine seriously the grammar and syntax of an older ornamental language. They come to the Museum hoping to see the lesson laid out. The present volume is an important element in our response to this demand, and there could be no better subject than the studious Robert Adam, archaeologist and entrepreneur, the most international of the great British architects, and an undoubted genius of European neo-classicism.

John Murdoch
Keeper of Designs, Prints & Drawings

Acknowledgements

In the preparation of this catalogue of drawings by or associated with the Adam brothers I have received help and kindness from many quarters. My first debt is to Michael Kauffmann both for suggesting that I might prepare this catalogue and for his patient understanding when a move from the University of Edinburgh to University College Dublin made the volume less prompt in its production than he or I had at first intended. In practical matters I have been greatly helped by members of the museum staff, particularly by Mr Michael Snodin of the Department of Designs, Prints and Drawings, editor of the series of catalogues of architectural drawings, by Mr Maurice Tomlin of the Department of Furniture and Interior Design, by Mr Martin Chapman who at an early stage made an original sorting of the Adam material and transcribed many inscriptions for me, and by Mr Hilary Young who carried out additional checks. No study of Robert and James Adam can be undertaken without reference to the main corpus of drawings held in Sir John Soane's Museum or to the Adam correspondence and family papers deposited in the Scottish Record Office in Edinburgh: in the Soane Museum I have been helped by Sir John Summerson, by Miss Dorothy Stroud, who answered particular queries on Henry Holland, and by Miss Christine Skull; I am also indebted to Mr Keith Adam of Blair Adam for permission to study and in some cases to take copies of manuscripts that are his property and to Sir John Clerk of Penicuik for similar permissions. I have had further help from the staff of the National Monuments Record for Scotland, particularly from Miss Kitty Cruft and Mr Ian Gow, who invariably manage to make research into Scottish architecture pleasurable, and from Mrs Eileen Harris and Dr Robin Middleton who have helped with the furniture and sketch designs. Thanks are also due to the owners of a number of Adam buildings who have put up with my visits and answered inquiries over many years, and to my colleagues, Dr Eileen Kane, who kindly read a draft of the introduction and to Honora Ni Chriogain and Blathnait Crowley who typed the text. I greatly value all this assistance and hope that the benefits are evident.

Alistair Rowan
Dublin, May 1984

Introduction

The Collection

The collection of architectural drawings by Robert Adam in the Victoria and Albert Museum is not large. Some 138 drawings are by the architect or may be attributed to his office or assistants; while a further 58 anonymous and other drawings, at various times described as 'Adam', reflect quite clearly the impact of his style on minor and other designers working in the late eighteenth century. Though it is not negligible, this total of 96 drawings (and one fake) may be put in context by comparison with the main bulk of Adam drawings, now in Sir John Soane's Museum, which, including a recently rediscovered volume of Italian sketches, runs to a total of 57 bound folio volumes containing some 8,785 sheets of drawings. The Adam drawings in the Soane Museum must constitute one of the most substantial collections of drawn material relating to the career of a British architect in the eighteenth century and even in the context of British architectural history as a whole, they are uniquely important. Students of Robert Adam's architecture must start with the Soane Museum Drawings and in the catalogue which follows frequent reference will be made to them.

A modest collection is not necessarily a dull one and, in the case of this more minor holding of Adam drawings, there are distinct advantages in its limitation of size. A catalogue of a few designs may examine each in more detail than is possible with thousands of drawings while, by a happy accident, the Museum's collection covers a wide range both of the architect's work and of the type of drawing that the practice of architecture gave rise to in eighteenth-century Britain. If we are here exploring a comparatively narrow seam in the accumulated deposits laid down by Adam's architectural activity it is still a rich one, well worth investigation.

The Career of Robert Adam

Robert Adam was born in Kirkcaldy in Scotland in 1728. He was the second son in a family of four brothers and six sisters and grew up in Edinburgh where his father, William Adam, was established as one of the principal builders in the city, as well as being an architect, merchant and wholesale supplier of builders' materials with warehouses at Leith. Robert, like many middle-class Scottish boys of his time, attended the University of Edinburgh without taking a degree and then joined his father in practice as an architect and builder, working with his elder brother John on government contracts for the Board of Ordnance in the Highlands, for the Duke of Argyll at Inveraray Castle and for the Earl of Hopetoun at Hopetoun House near Edinburgh. In 1748 when their father died John and Robert continued in practice together where in time they were joined by James, the third brother, who was Robert's junior by four years. The determination to excel – one of the most remarkable characteristics of William Adam – was inherited in full measure by his sons, particularly by Robert and James. While John, as head of the family, was content to fill the position of an architect in Scotland and to develop the estate of Blair Adam, purchased by his father near Kinross, the younger brothers set their sights higher. It was their intention to become the leading architects for the whole of Great Britain, not just for Edinburgh or for Scotland, and this objective they very largely achieved. There can be no doubt that the success which the brothers encountered was due, for the most part, to the originality, inventive talent and even the capacity for plain hard work of Robert. His is the dominant personality in the Adam's architectural achievement. It was he who took the first steps that were to establish the brothers as the leaders of fashionable taste in London in the early years of the reign of George III and it was his energy that maintained that position for the next twenty years.

The key to Robert Adam's success lies in his decision to make the grand tour to Italy in 1754. He travelled with the Hon. Charles Hope, a brother of the Earl of Hopetoun, in whose company he could gain an entrée both to places and to society that might not otherwise have been accessible to a Scottish builder's son. Adam was fully aware of these advantages. Though he and Hope were to part company some months after their arrival in Rome, by the time they did so his reputation as a gentleman of private means, and as a connoisseur, was made. He was to remain in Italy until the Autumn of 1757, a period of three and a quarter years, during which time he had, on his own admission, to unlearn what he knew of architecture and of drawing in Scotland and to begin his professional studies afresh. It is this decision more than any other which offers a measure of Adam's integrity as an artist. He was 26 when he left for Italy and almost 30 when he returned. With his brother John he had already conducted architectural works of a very substantial sort. He was a man in whose make up self esteem was liberally mixed and yet he had the candour, on contact with antiquity and with the architectural thought of the French and Papal academies, to identify both in his background and in the architectural work of his family, ideas that were provincial and out-of-date. In Rome the social metamorphosis from builder's son to connoisseur was accompanied by an even more remarkable intellectual transformation in which the know-how of a local expertise was replaced by an understanding of a profoundly different character. Adam, by the time he left, knew Roman architecture as a totality. He knew its concepts and the particulars of its preferred plan forms. He understood contemporary archaeological evidence and, in drawing the details of architectural fragments, learnt at first hand something of the free elaboration of Imperial decorative inventiveness, so different from the codified, yet formally correct, classicism of the sixteenth-century Italian pattern books on which he had been trained.

Two men played a vital role in the architect's education at this time: the French architect and architectural draughtsman, Jacques Louis Clérisseau, and the Venetian architect and archaeologist, Giovanni Battista Piranesi. Clérisseau was to teach Adam an entirely new style of architectural drawing, travelling with him to visit antiquities and remaining in his employment as a salaried draughtsman as long as Adam was in Italy. Piranesi is described by Adam as his 'extraordinary genius', the greatest engraver of views of Rome and of Roman antiquities of the whole century, a dealer in antiquities, and an architectural and archaeological polemicist of irresistible charm. From time to time Adam provided financial assistance for Piranesi to further his archaeological publications. He was repaid by laudatory references included in different plates and by the dedication of Piranesi's *Campus Martius* (frontispiece), yet these business arrangements with the French artist and the Italian archaeologist did not apparently obtrude on the personal friendships that developed between the three men. Adam and his chosen tutors became close friends.

Adam returned to London in January 1758 where, with three of his sisters as housekeepers, he set up in practice as an architect. A single man with cultivated interests, well informed and articulate was no doubt as welcome to eighteenth-century society in London as he would be today. Adam, according to his contemporaries, had great charm of manner. He was confident in his taste and confident too in the superiority of his understanding of what classicism was all about. He had drawings – his own and others – and a collection of antiquities, tastefully disposed in the entrance hall of his house, to attest to the probity of his position. Very soon he was taken up by society and had begun to win wealthy clients.

The decade of the brothers' major achievement was the 1760s. Through the patronage of the Scotch party in government, notably the Earl of Bute and the Duke of Argyll, Robert was made joint architect to the King's works with Sir William Chambers in 1761. Lord Bute, who in the early stages of George III's reign was Prime Minister, employed Adam to design a large town house in Berkeley Square and a new country mansion at Luton Hoo in Bedfordshire. At Kedleston in Derbyshire, Adam replaced James Paine and Matthew

Brettingham as the architect for a large Palladian house which, by subtle touches, he recast in a different Neo-classical mould. At Harewood it was John Carr of York who ceded his position to the new genius of classical interior decoration, while commissions for substantial and sumptuous remodellings amounting effectively to new work came in the home counties from the Duke of Northumberland at Syon (1762); from the banker Robert Child at Osterley (1765); from Lord Shelburne at Bowood (1761) and from Lord Mansfield at Kenwood (1767). While Robert was building up the practice that led to these commissions, James, as his brother had done, was making a grand tour, disputing with Piranesi and mastering the art of drawing with the help of Clérisseau. He left London in 1760 and returned to join Robert in practice in 1763. By then the Adam office in Lower Grosvenor Street had become a large one with several clerks and draughtsmen besides the brothers themselves.

James's return probably removed some of the pressure from his elder brother. For the rest of their careers he seems to have taken over much of the day to day responsibilities of the firm and often acted as the businessman in the brothers' affairs. About this time the youngest Adam boy, William, joined Robert and James in business, not however in their practice as architects but as a partner in a firm of developers and builders' suppliers, William Adam & Co. (which also included John Adam in Edinburgh), and which was set up in 1764. The greater leisure occasioned by James's return also enabled Robert to complete his one great contribution to classical archaeology, a survey of the fortified city palace built by Diocletian at Split in Dalmatia, which Robert had surveyed in six weeks of intense activity in the summer of 1757 shortly before he left Italy. *The Ruins of the Palace of the Emperor Diocletian at Spalatro* was published in 1764 with sumptuous engraved plates and was used by Robert, as Piranesi's publications had been before, as a form of quality publicity to keep his name and abilities fresh in the minds of potential patrons. The brothers were always conscious of the benefits of a public image. They sent drawings of recent work to be included in Woolfe and Gandon's continuation of *Vitruvius Britannicus* in 1767 and 1772; they issued plates of individual works separately, such as the Admiralty screen in Whitehall or the Adelphi overlooking the Thames, and then in 1773 they brought out the first part of the three volumes of their own designs published under the title *The Works in Architecture of Robert and James Adam.*

By the date *The Works* appeared Robert had been in practice in London for fifteen years and James for ten. There was no lack of work for they were much employed in the 1770s in the design of some minutely detailed and extravagantly finished aristocratic town houses yet they had begun to lose ground. A rising generation of younger architects who could copy their style – notably James Wyatt – was taking business from them, for the price of being in high fashion, as the Adams had been, is that sooner or later the fashionable world will find a new focus for its enthusiam. In the world of interior decoration, where the brothers had achieved some of their most spectacular successes, this is particularly true and so a note of self assertion, even criticism of others, appears in the letterpress of *The Works*: 'The novelty and variety of the following designs will, we flatter ourselves, not only excuse, but justify our conduct in communicating them to the world. We have not trod in the path of others, nor derived aid from their labours. In the works which we have had the honour to execute we not only met with the approbation of our employers but even with the imitation of other artists, to such a degree as in some measure to have brought about, in this country, a kind of revolution in the whole system of this useful and elegant art'. Many of Adam's contemporaries found the tone of this intolerable and there can be no doubt that from the mid 1770s the brothers met with increasing criticism where before they had only encountered praise. In this period financial worries were also to place a strain on the relations between the Adams in London and their family at home and these worries were to some extent a by-product of Robert and James's activities as architects.

In the opinion of John Adam, who by the end of his life was hardly on speaking terms with any of his brothers, it was their ungovernable ambition and greed that brought their name into disrepute yet the beginning of the Adam's difficulties lay in a wholly admirable and in a sense even public spirited development that they began through William Adam & Co. in 1768. This was the Adelphi, a scheme to redevelop a derelict and run-down area of London between the Strand and the river, with an impressive show front of eleven houses treated as a single terrace that overlooked the Thames. Streets behind this terrace, Adam Street, Robert Street and John Adam Street, accommodated a further 58 houses, and to bring the Adelphi to the level of the Strand the entire development was set on a massive two-storey podium of warehouse buildings with a complicated system of underground streets linking the riverside wharfs with the city's roads. As a private development the scale of the Adelphi scheme was unparalleled yet the resources which the brothers brought to their speculation were almost as spectacular. At this time William Adam & Co. had grown to employ between 2,000 and 3,000 tradesmen and labourers. It owned timber yards at Thames Bank, brick-works in London and Essex and was the contractor for paving the city of Westminster and seven London parishes. There is therefore no doubt that Robert and James, as well as being architects, in their capacity as partners of the family company, directed the largest single building empire in eighteenth-century Britain. It is wholly in character that they should do so and yet, while the company was at its most extended on its vast Adelphi project, that empire all but collapsed. Credit notes and paper money were the cause of this near failure for in financing its operations the firm had taken full advantage of both, only to be caught by a run on Scottish credit in 1772, caused by the failure of several private banks, that left the financial world in an uproar and the Adams stretched well beyond their means. In the event their company remained solvent though its affairs were, at best, strained and much of the brothers' time was taken up with financial matters. In March 1774 the Adelphi was disposed of as a lottery leaving William Adam & Co. once more financially sound.

Eighteenth-century London was not the sort of place in which such a spectacular near disaster could pass unnoticed. Robert and James Adam were too big and outwardly too successful. Inevitably their enterprise attracted criticism. People who had resented their methods as developers now enjoyed their embarrassments and the brothers emerged from the Adelphi affair with damaged reputations. Nor did their subsequent activity as partners in William Adam & Co. do anything to restore them in public esteem. Cheated, as they felt they had been, of one fortune, Robert, James and William proceeded to invest the company funds in other dubious schemes: speculative developments in Marylebone, Portland Place and Fitzroy Square; a patent cement, invented by a Swiss clergyman, Liardet, that would allow rich architectural detail to be reproduced cheaply in stucco; a cheap saltpetre factory, based on a process invented by a Flemish chemist, J. P. de Bruges, which had it worked must have assured for William Adam & Co. an effective monopoly of the manufacture of gun powder for the whole of the United Kingdom. Whatever seemed to offer a prospect of quick profit found the Adams in London ready with their funds. In their defence it may be said that each of these projects was in an area closely connected with their professional pursuits as architects, yet John Adam, who was unwittingly drawn into their financial troubles, was forced to sell his villa at North Merchiston outside Edinburgh and to put the family estate of Blair Adam on the market, believed they had been corrupted quite simply by the lure of great wealth. From the mid 1770s until the end of the century the brothers' company operated at a loss. Only its scale can have saved them from the disaster which came ultimately with the bankruptcy of the only surviving brother, William, in 1801.

It is against this background of financial expectation and recurrent disappointment that Robert and James's later activities as architects must be set. While the Adelphi was building they moved there and moved their office to a house in Robert Street. Later when the development had become an embarrassment they removed again to 13 Albemarle Street, close to the fashionable centre of the city and there they remained for the rest of their lives.

Robert Adam, despite his appointment as joint architect of the King's works, never received significant patronage from the Crown and few opportunities to design public buildings in England: Sir William Chambers, the other joint architect of the King's works, disliked him and as Chambers had been drawing tutor to George III, as Prince of Wales, no doubt he used his influence to keep Adam pretensions within bounds. In Scotland however the position was different. There Robert and James were thought of as men of genius who had brought distinction to their country and in the 1770s and 1780s Scottish commissions accounted for an increasing proportion of their work. From about 1775 Robert made annual visits to Edinburgh and opened an office there to look after the Scottish side of the practice. No lack of commissions marred the architects' last years but the strain of their unfortunate affairs as developers took its toll. Robert became touchy and quarrelsome, all too ready to take disputes to court, overbearing and impatient. He suffered increasingly from ill health and from a state of mind which made him appear to his sisters to work too hard and too long. He died suddenly in his house in London on 3 March 1792 to be followed by James in October 1794.

The Drawings

The drawings by Robert Adam, now in the museum's collection, cover almost every stage of the architect's career. Carefully examined they may illustrate three things: Adam's interests as a designer; the range of types of drawing that he regularly employed, and something of the development of his architectural style. Occasionally they may also offer some insights into the realities of the architect's life. This is very much the case with some of the earliest drawings, the sketches and academic exercises produced by Adam in his twenties when he first studied in Rome. These drawings are of various sorts: careful academic studies of architectural elements, such as the highly finished enriched column base (cat. 2), and picturesque compositions of fragments (cat. 3) or of imaginary Roman ruins (cat. 15). There are exploratory studies of architectural systems, a Michelangelesque play with interlocking orders that fascinated Adam all his life (cat. 10) and sketch designs done in an early enthusiasm for the 'Antique' compositions of Piranesi (cat. 15, 16) or the lessons of antiquity as explained by Clérisseau. Two quick pen elevations of the interiors of ruined temples partially restored are inscribed by Adam in French, one with the charming conceit that the temple had been frequented by a hermit who converted it into a chapel (cat. 7, 8), but here the young architect's command of French is not up to such complex ideas and he has had several shots at the inscription or perhaps Clérisseau has corrected it for him! Elsewhere we catch a glimpse of the two men working together when Adam, by now fully familiar with the concatenated symmetries of the ideal designs of the French Academy, scribbles down in pencil – it is no more than that – the idea of a grand public building, with its principal elevation set down in ink below (cat. 6). Adam perhaps leaves the room and while he is out Clérisseau writes on this small design a grandiloquent inscription commensurate with its architectural pretensions, 'I approve of this project made in Rome in the year of grace one thousand seven hundred and seventy-seven' and signs it with an elaborate flourish. Here surely we encounter in all its vitality the high spirits of young men who feel confident of the future and fancy that in their command of the current architectural idiom they hold the keys for future success.

Of all the architects working in Britain in the eighteenth century Robert Adam was perhaps the most artistic. Kent might just dispute the title but for Adam drawing became as natural a means of communication as speech; perhaps at times even more, an aid to mental processes and to the clarification of his ideas. The theoretical and sketch designs that he made in Italy demonstrate clearly the extent to which he would try out ideal notions on paper and indeed the attraction of a perfectly centralised or geometrical plan – a triangle or a polygon – with which he first experimented in Rome, remained with him all his life. Many of the early student schemes are pasted into one of the volumes in the Soane Museum which bears at drawings Nos 72 and 73 the inscription 'the sketches before this were done abroad, those that follow are done since my return to England, January 1758'. It seems clear from the care Adam took to preserve such scraps that he would, from time to time, draw inspiration from his early work as from a reservoir of ideas. The relationship between a sketch design and a finished drawing is nicely illustrated within the Museum's collection, for both the elevations of the restored interiors of a ruined temple, referred to above, formed the basis for one very handsome section of a design for a ruin similar to the domed and vaulted interiors of brick at Hadrian's Villa at Tivoli which Adam had drawn while abroad. In this scheme both sketches are reproduced, now in the more finished form of a presentation drawing, flanking a Pantheon-like central hall (cat. 61). It was drawings such as this design, the elaborate column base, or the careful architectural records made for Adam by other artists (cat. 4), which he would use to persuade potential clients of the superiority of his knowledge and taste on his return to London. Sir Nathaniel Curzon was shown some portfolios when he visited Adam in Grosvenor Street and promised, after perusing the drawings he had made in Italy, to employ him at Kedleston.

In 34 years of independent practice Robert never lost the habit of sketching: designs sprang from his mind onto the page rapidly blocked out in pencil (cat. 10) or drawn boldly in sepia ink (cat. 30). In both we sense the confidence of absolute proficiency. There is nothing hesitant about his draughtsmanship and his imagination never flags. There is of course a sense of continuity – the identifiable idiom of the Adam style in elevations, interiors, wall monuments or plasterwork – but Adam's architecture is not a static repetition of a few fixed formulae. The idiom is modified according to the class of building or the date of a design and even within one period and class of subject the potential for variety is great. One sheet of designs for plasterwork decorations (cat. 35), or an early variant for the arabesques in the famous Etruscan room at Osterley (cat. 101), may illustrate the fecundity of the architect's decorative imagination and even perhaps his reluctance, which is a marked feature of Adam as a designer, to settle finally on any solution.

Sketches that are exploratory studies of plan forms or of decorative patterns make up one category among the freehand drawings produced by Adam in developing his ideas. Another is the picturesque perspective view. Both brothers were well aware of the variety of effects which might be created in architecture by the viewpoint from which a building was seen. Their stress in the preface to *The Works* – their only piece of coherent architectural theory – on 'movement' makes this clear and a recurrent theme in their layout of an interior – at Syon, the gallery at Newby, or Home House – is the manipulation of a visitor's impressions by a carefully contrived sequence of perspectival effects so that even the interior of an aristocratic house may take on picturesque quality. That the picturesque appealed strongly to Robert Adam is clear from the quantity of his drawings that survive depicting buildings in their setting. From the Italian period there are the topographical sketches of Tivoli and other Roman sites – none of these in the museum's collection – and many imaginary compositions of antique ruins in the manner of Vanvitelli and more especially of the Roman *vedutista* G. B. Pannini (cat. 15). On his return to Britain Adam was frequently to propose ruin pieces of this sort as an integral part of interior decorative schemes (cat. 88, 91). Later in his practice he also developed the habit of filling out the elevations of his less formal designs, particularly at the stage of sketches, with a landscape setting. This may be illustrated by the painterly elevation of a rustic bridge (cat. 29), the bath house at Mistley (cat. 143), the sketch of a rustic thatched house, shown in an evocative wooded landscape with lochs, hillock and a busy sky (cat. 30) and two designs for eye-catcher castles, a huge ruin for Robert Child at Osterley (cat. 108) and a garden tower for Duncan Davidson at Cromarty (cat. 144). It should be noted however that all these designs remain architectural drawings. Their intention is to set out in elevational form the proposed appearance of a building and, if they are to be worked out fully, they will be elaborated to accord with plans drawn to a specific scale and with other detailed drawings necessary for their construction. Adam, with the eye of a painter, seeks to give his sketch elevations context but they remain as elevations with all the flatness of effect that this convention in technical drawing dictates.

Such pictorially elaborated architectural drawings are always quite distinct from the last remaining category of Adam freehand design, the romantic landscape or landscape with a fortified town or castle, which constitutes a pictorial genre in its own right. Very occasionally the boundary between an architectural design and an ideal picturesque composition seems to be eroded. In the museum's collection there are two light free sketches (cat. 17) where the main lines of a landscape are broadly blocked out, with a rotunda, in the tradition of Kent's Temple of Ancient Virtue at Stowe, or the circular garden building erected by Adam on rising ground to the west of the main house at Audley End. But we cannot say that these designs *are* designs for any building scheme by Adam and too much should not be made of the possible link between his romantic views and the type of evocative architecture, particularly the castle style, that assumed such importance in the later stages of his career. Of the numerous picturesque landscapes which Adam produced in the 1770s and 1780s none relate exactly to any architecture built by the brothers. The same forms appear – fat round towers with machicolated wall heads and low conical roofs, round-arched doorways, crenellated walls – but it is only the mood that is common both to their work as architects and to Robert's poetic vision as an artist.

The picturesque drawings, more than any other designs by the architect, may take us into the mind of Robert Adam (James so far as is known did not indulge himself in this vein), and in so far as they represent Adam in moments of relaxation, devising dramatic landscapes or crowning hills with an evocative silhouette, they illustrate in a most vivid form the aesthetic sensibilities of the architect. Here he appears as very much a man of his time. The subtle gradation of tones, the golden, almost balmy light, the theatrical contrasts of intense shadow and brilliant illumination, are aspects of the landscape explored in the same years by Gainsborough, Richard Wilson and the Rev. William Gilpin. At times the Adam picturesque drawings may seem to be produced to a formula, with Poussinesque foreground figures, the main interest in the middle distance and usually a background of hills; but we should remember Wilson's matter-of-fact description of some of his own subjects as 'good breeders'. The search for originality, or an individual character that is strongly marked, is not a significant element in eighteenth-century art. It is the ability to vary and to refine that Adam's contemporaries admired. A considerable range of mood is achieved in the four romantic views by Adam in this collection and one, the hilltop castle by a lake (cat. 26), is a most beautiful example of his response to light and of his creative ability in the exacting medium of watercolour.

The office drawings of Robert and James are clearly different from any sketches or free hand designs. Their lines are ruled, they are drawn to a scale which is usually marked on the page and often they are rendered with carefully graded washes which have cast shadows of a darker tone. Drawings from the start of Adam's practice, from the late 1750s and early 1760s, are usually by Robert himself for at this stage of his career he would hardly have entrusted the presentation of his ideas to an assistant. These early drawings are characterised by warm pale washes of a delicate character and the lines of the architecture are very thinly drawn. Designs in the Soane Museum for the Admiralty Screen in Whitehall of 1759, for a gateway for Lord Kinnoull of 1761 and for Moor Park of 1763, are typical of Adam's architectural draughtsmanship in these early years. The style is represented in the museum's collection by the two contract drawings for Compton Verney of 1761 (cat. 53, 54) and by the first scheme for Osterley prepared in 1761 for Francis Child (cat. 76–80). In later work, for example the East front or the Greenhouse at Osterley (cat. 103) made for Robert Child, there is, for all the skill of the renderings, a certain hardness, a tendency to use dense black for the windows and a mechanical quality which suggests that by the mid 1760s the preparation of drawings, and even the finishing of sets of designs for presentation to clients, was left to senior assistants in Grosvenor Street who were trained in the office style. By 1770 the possibility of a fully rendered elevation or plan being finished by Adam himself becomes remote though as head of the office the architect continues to sign and date most of the drawings his assistants produce. Titles on the office drawings are written in a standard elegant copperplate that tends to disguise individual hands; sometimes it is very like Robert Adam's own handwriting; sometimes, as in the ruin design for Osterley (cat. 108) it is not. The only differences that can regularly be noted are those between an inscription on a drawing that was to be sent out and the more careless writing on a copy design that was to stay in the office.

To some extent, the organisation of the brothers' office can be reconstructed from the collections of their drawings. Dust marks on the back of innumerable designs make it clear that the drawings for an individual scheme or client were kept rolled up in open shelves with abbreviated inscriptions and a number for reference, often in red ink, written on the edge of the back as 'Lord Holland's Gateway, Number 12' or 'Bridge for Mr. Stirling Number twenty-six'. That the sketches are substantially the work of the brothers is proved by the occurrence of brief notes jotted down in Adam's hand on the back of several sheets in the Soane Museum: 'Lord March/George Johnstone wishes to see Mr Brem & Mrs. Hogarth/ Signing papers at Blakes & Co/Friday, dinner at the British [Coffee House]' or 'Saturday night to dine with Mrs. Home at Admiralty to [be] there at 3.o'clock/to be with Lady Apsley Saturday morning 10 o'clock/The leases of Mansfield Street stop[ped] on account of Mr. West objecting to/What is the cause and get the Duke [of] Portland to settle it'. Such personal memoranda bring us very close to the day to day workings in the office, with Adam perhaps in the middle of some problem of a design, running over in his mind what else has to be done.

The scale on which the brothers operated, and perhaps also the fact that many of their schemes were carried out over a period of ten, twelve, or even more years, necessitated the keeping of proper records. The system in their office was well organised and appears to have anticipated many of the standard practices that developed in the nineteenth century. Their systematic numbering of drawings, at least for the designs that were kept in the office, is a case in point as is their regular practice of keeping copy drawings of designs that were sent out. Often these were only partly completed with symmetrical elements left out or shown only as pencil roughs. Elsewhere the office copy will be an almost fully rendered design but one that bears scribbled alterations added in soft pencil by Adam and here we may assume that the design which was sent to the client was redrawn to incorporate the architect's alterations. Occasionally, as is the case of the Triumphal Doric Gateway (cat. 11) a note is added by a clerk to record the difference between 'the fair copy' and the design that has been kept for reference. The office copies often give extra information about the date the fair copy was sent, to whom, whether it was shown or not, and whether it was referred to in Adam's correspondence to his client.

Though recipes for making tracing paper exist from the late eighteenth century its use was not general until the 1840s or 1850s and Adam's clerks reproduced his drawings by the regular practice of pricking through a design. Several in the museum's collection have small holes in the paper showing that the design was set out in this way while a drawing in the Soane Museum of a screen for Portland House carries the brief but precise note 'Duke of Portland. pricked out from those that are kept from No 8'.

In one respect the drawings in the museum offer a wider range of type than is represented by the much larger collection in the Soane Museum. We have, in the magnificent set of drawings that were produced for Robert Child at Osterley (cat. 81–108), some supreme examples of Adam's 'fair copies', a type of drawing which necessarily does not feature in the Soane Museum collection as that originated in what remained in the brothers' office at the time of James's death. The client's drawings for Lord Lisburne at Mamhead (cat. 113–137) are another set of designs which in their finish far excel any of the office copies of schemes for the house though, as Lord Lisburne was a less munificent patron than Child and, after several approaches to Adam, appears to have done nothing or very little, the quality of the finish of the drawings – which represent alternative schemes – is far less. Adam may well have worked on the Osterley drawings himself; in the Mamhead set there are clearly two different draughtsmen at work and we may assume that this less distinguished job was for the most part given to Adam's clerks to draw up.

In many cases major works undertaken by the brothers grew out of commissions for alterations or additions to existing buildings, especially country houses. This was the origin of their proposals for Mamhead. Among the drawings for the house are two floor plans (cat. 123, 124) which are a survey of the old building, possibly by a local hand, on which Adam has noted such practical considerations as what walls can stand and which will have to be new, whether a light can be got to an attic room through an old window or that a vaulted wine cellar cannot be removed without disturbing the floor above. For all their humdrum practicality these drawings were noted by the architect in a way that suggests a combination of his proposals and the client's instructions while he was at the house. Such survey plans were an essential part of the architect's job and, as they involved the careful examination of a structure whose state was bound to influence any proposals that might be made, they could not be delegated to assistants in the office. Once settled, design proposals for alterations could be drawn up by clerks. Then if the work went ahead the office might be called upon to produce precise working drawings for the tradesmen to use on the site. The progression to working drawings did not necessarily follow. On occasions Adam merely made a charge for his designs and left his patron to come to an agreement with a local builder independently of the architect. Elsewhere, if the conduct of the work were under his control, he would supply detailed drawings as the construction proceeded for which he would charge a percentage of the total cost of the building work, initially three and later five per cent. Working drawings from the Adam office are comparatively few. In this collection there are the two contract drawings for Compton Verney already mentioned and two details for ironwork – a fanlight for the Drapers' Hall, which is priced (cat. 62) and the stair rail for Gawthorp (or Harewood) House (cat. 60) – which also seem to come into this category. The Gawthorp drawing has the additional interest of having been folded to letter size, perhaps when it was sent out from the office.

The normal function of a fully rendered drawing is to capture the enthusiasm of a client by the skilful and attractive presentation of the proposals. Occasionally it may also be made for the use of another artist as in the drawings for stained glass at Croome Church or for chimneypieces of statuary marble (cat. 56, 57). One other use represented in the museum's collection is the design that is prepared for publication as an engraving. The magnificent perspective view of the gallery at Syon, fully coloured and enlivened by washes and cast shadows that suggest a sudden burst of sunlight flooding into the room is one of the most handsome drawings ever made for the brothers (cat. 111). It is reproduced exactly in *The Works*, Vol. III, pl. II, though unfortunately neither the draughtsman nor the engraver is recorded. Several specialist artists who worked for the Adams in London might have produced this handsome interior view. A second design that was to be engraved is the straightforward plan of the garden alcove for the Duke of Montagu at Richmond (cat. 112) which is published in *The Works*, Vol. II, as the lower part of plate VIII. It has been suggested that the large scale elevations of the late classical villa designed by the brothers at Wyreside (cat. 145–147) may also have been prepared for publication in George Richardson's *New Vitruvius Britannicus* though if this was ever the Adams' intention their designs were not in the end used.

The Adam Style

The perspective view of the gallery at Syon (cat. 111) illustrates succinctly what many people regard as the essential Adam style. The interior is delicate yet decorated with such a profusion of ornament that few surfaces are left unadorned. Individual elements of the decorative scheme are all classically derived: the plasterwork panels, the ribbon bands and the figure medallions of the ceiling; the rinceaux and arabesques (or grotesques) on the pilasters; or the strigil – the S-curved fluting – on the cupboard below the bookshelves. The profiles of cornices and the plinths of the pilasters are refined until they project minimally and thus the whole room offers an antithesis to the massively architectural taste of the British Palladian School in which Adam first trained. This delicate surface character with only shallow projections is repeated in the Osterley interiors, in the ceilings at Bowood or for Mr Devall (cat. 5, 70, 71) and it is represented in external architecture in the screen designed for Lord Holland (cat. 72). When Robert and James wrote in the Introduction to *The Works* of their 'beautiful variety of light mouldings, gracefully formed and delicately enriched' it was this sort of architecture that they described. Their published work, taken as a whole, tends to reinforce the impression that this is *the* Adam style and certainly it was this manner that was seized upon both by their imitators and by those who grew tired of their taste. To talk of Adam's style as 'gingerbread and sippets of embroidery' or of ceilings as enlivened with 'cheesecakes and raspberry tarts', as some contemporary critics did, might unkindly describe some aspects of this decorative style;[4] but there is more to the Adams' work as architects, and a far greater range of effect, than a concentration on their most famous interiors might suggest.

Firstly we should note that the brothers described their new ornaments as 'arranged with propriety and skill'. This is a valid claim for there is never anything haphazard – as there can be with Adam's imitators – in the arrangement of their decorations. The gallery at Syon may be understated architecturally but it remains an architectural design with an absolutely consistent use of such architectural elements as Adam sees fit to employ. The long internal wall is articulated by groups of four Corinthian pilasters arranged in a pattern of narrow, wide and narrow intervals. This rhythm is picked up by the spacing of the niches on either side of the doorcases and the chimney-piece and it appears again in elevation at the extreme end of the room so that, for those who can discern it, a satisfyingly coherent theme runs through the whole room. In a similar way the horizontals of the design are respected absolutely: the cornice of the chair rail and the pedestals of the pilasters are used to establish a clear visual base while the cornice and frieze below the pediments of the doors provide a second strong horizontal linked continuously with the cornice and frieze that forms the top of the bookcase recesses between the pilasters. In these recesses Adam provides a 'logical' support for this frieze by the introduction of a minor Ionic order appearing as a quarter pilaster against the side of the larger Corinthian shaft and this secondary Ionic system is used consistently along the whole length of the window wall. Thus while the details of the room seem infinitely delicate Adam has provided a stronger structure, on a larger scale, which like the bars in a musical score underlies and stiffens the surface pattern. In the gallery at Syon he is first and foremost an architect and one for whom the details of antique plasterwork, for all their novelty, take second place.

Exterior elevations by Adam in the museum's collection are comparatively few. There are drawings of schemes for four country houses of which only one – the first house proposed at Osterley – is completely described. There are also three sets of gate lodges; a triumphal archway and a greenhouse. By good fortune the range of date is widely spread so that a comparison of the façades may illustrate some of the changes that took place in Adam's architecture. The early houses, Compton Verney (1760) and the first scheme for Osterley (1761) are still strongly Palladian (cat. 54, 77–79). Adam proposes Corinthian porticoes of a giant order as the focus of the entrance front of each house. He reproduces such Palladian conventions as a rusticated basement, the main floor window sill treated as a continuous stringcourse, the 'floating' square window above, and at each house the windows are framed by regular architraves. Two of the proposals for the new North front at Mamhead (cat. 125, 126), made in the later 1760s, are not essentially different though the third design, the West elevation and the proposed offices (cat. 127–129) introduce us to the more severe manner of Adam's mature work in which the frames round the windows disappear and window openings are left unadorned as a simple negation of the wall surface. This treatment is common to many Adam designs; it appears in Osterley as designed for Robert Child after 1765 (cat. 81–83).

In later work Adam also tends to employ a calculated contrast in his elevations between plain surfaces of undecorated ashlar and finely wrought sections of carved decoration. The gates for the Deputy Ranger's Lodge in the Green Park (cat. 68) and for Osterley (cat. 102) both illustrate this development and employ a characteristic Adam frieze of repetitive deep flutings which is also found in a number of his interior designs. In the Osterley gates the lodges are designed as two perfect cubes with vaulted pyramid roofs and this preference for pure geometric forms in formal work is strikingly displayed in the proposals for an arched gateway in London (cat. 69). The gateway is one of Adam's most heroic designs. It is built up of elements which, though massively scaled, are perfectly inter-related with a simple, coherent logic. We note again in this design Adam's careful balance between ornament and emphatic masonry which here is given extra weight by the use of heavy rustication across the entire façade. Clearly this is architecture in a very different mode from Lord Holland's delicate screen in Piccadilly or the light-hearted conservatory at Osterley with its succession of prettily overlapping Venetian windows built in a bow across the front.

Two schemes from the last years of Adam's life may illustrate the changes that took place in his architectural taste: these are the gateway for Gosford House (cat. 58) and the additions proposed for Wyreside, which constitute a virtual rebuilding of the old house (cat. 145–147). While each design displays the architect's continued interest in geometrical composition and, in the case of Wyreside, a building up of masses on an additive method that seems to go back to his student days in Rome, each is patently a design of the end of the century. At Gosford Adam adopts the modern taste for Greek Doric columns, baseless and with fluted shafts, and at Wyreside he makes extensive use of a tripartite window framed in an aedicule and set within a relieving arch which in his earlier years would certainly – as in the first scheme for Osterley – have contained a Venetian window. This shift to flat-headed tripartite windows is characteristic of English architecture in the late eighteenth century. Adam is here, perhaps unconsciously, adapting his design to a prevailing trend yet the scheme as a whole still bears the indelible stamp of the architect's personality: the sphinxes, the saucer dome terminal pavilions, the frameless window openings, a certain innate sense of proportion in the elevations and, above all, the scrupulous inter-relationship of parts – as in the gallery at Syon – give it an architectural authority that is uniquely his.

Adamesque

By 1780 many minor designers throughout Britain and Ireland had taken over some of the more obvious features of the Adam decorative style: thin profiles, geometrically patterned ceilings, friezes made up of alternating anthemia and lotus flowers, or of vases, putti and griffons. They freely invented 'antique' capitals and attempted the general delicate effect that is the hallmark of what we might call the brothers' drawing room manner. What is lacking in the work of these anonymous figures is the sense of structure that dominates even the brothers' most intricate designs: while they found a fresh vocabulary in the Adams' decorative work they lacked an understanding of its syntax. This is not a criticism that can be applied to the Adams' major rivals in decorative work, to James Paine, James Stuart or, a little later, to James Wyatt, who became their most distinguished imitator. Paine and Stuart have a distinctive taste and so does Wyatt whose designs, while superficially like Adam work, display a greater restraint. There is behind much of Adam's decorative design an inventive fecundity that seems almost to have its roots in the rococo: Wyatt's inspiration always remains more chaste. Lessons of restraint were lost on minor men. That they saw only the delicacy and decorative freedom of the brothers' manner may be illustrated by the Adamesque designs published in the pattern books of figures like John Crunden and William Pain. Here artistic freedom – the right that Adam claimed for every man of genius – has become in the hands of lesser architects an excuse for loose or ill-contrived design. Such a character may be traced in many minor decorative schemes – built interiors or paper proposals – whose designers are now unknown. Adam style chimneypieces, which have Adamesque decorations yet are unlike Adam's own designs, abound in the later eighteenth century and were obviously produced in large quantity. The brothers' device of screening the end of a room with a pair of columns, given prominence in their published work, becomes by 1800 a cliché of speculative building and of minor architects alike. Usually it is accompanied by thin Adamesque plasterwork and by the six panel mahogany doors that the brothers put into so many of their schemes.

The Origins of the Collection

With the exception of the designs for Compton Verney, Mamhead and Osterley – a total of 60 drawings – virtually all the Robert Adam material in the museum's collection shares a common provenance from the collection of Charles James Richardson, an articled clerk in Sir John Soane's office from 1824 to 1830 and subsequently an assistant there until Soane's death in 1837. In 1833 Soane obtained an Act of Parliament to turn his house and its collections into a museum and in the same year purchased for £200, 56 bound volumes of Adam's architectural drawings which arrived in the museum in July that year. The Adam collection which had been sorted and organised into volumes probably over a period of years, beginning about 1796, had been the source of a good deal of trouble to the surviving members of the brothers' family and finally to their niece, Susan Clerk, by whom it was sold to Soane. It had been in existence, firstly in London and later in Edinburgh, for 30 or 35 years before it reached Lincoln's Inn Fields and no doubt some drawings had been removed and gaps created before Soane took custody of it. After Soane's death, the first curator of the museum, George Bailey, who had been Soane's chief clerk and Richardson's immediate superior, made a hand list at the beginning of each volume but a complete index was not prepared, nor the drawings stamped and numbered, until the curatorship of Walter Spiers who catalogued the Adam collection between 24 August 1908 and 19 April 1909. By this time a significant number of gaps had appeared from which it is evident that throughout the nineteenth century a number of unscrupulous collectors have helped themselves to Adam designs from the Soane Museum. It seems clear now that C. J. Richardson was one of these.

The evidence against Richardson, if not conclusive, is substantial. At some stage before the drawings left the Adam family, a list of contents for twenty-three of the volumes with an alphabetical index of clients was drawn up. Though the numbering of the volumes as they are now is not the same as in this Adam index the two sets of numbers may be easily collated and the contents match. The volumes in question are the later series in Soane's numbering from 28 to 51. These deal with schemes for buildings as opposed to interior designs or sketches and from them six clients may be identified whose commissions are also represented by drawings from Richardson's collection now in the Victoria and Albert Museum. These are John Fenton Cawthorn, the Earl of Coventry, Duncan Davidson, Lord William Gordon, the Duke of Montagu and the Earl of Wemyss. The Adam index lists the number of drawings or 'pieces' relating to each of these clients and in every case it appears that there were once more drawings in the collection than now remain in the Soane Museum volumes. Where there were five designs for Mr Cawthorn's house there are now only two; three drawings for Lord Coventry's gate become two; six designs for Mr Davidson's castle-style tower become five; Lord William Gordon's gateway is reduced from three to two drawings; the Duke of Montagu's seat, originally two drawings, becomes one; the drawings for Lord Wemyss's gate design are similarly reduced from two to one. Now in each case the number of drawings missing from the Soane Museum collection is supplied exactly by the designs that Richardson sold to the Victoria and Albert Museum so we are left with the inescapable conclusion that these drawings were taken out of the Adam volumes. Whether Richardson was the culprit is not of course proved though the balance of probability points to him.

The theft of Adam's drawings from the Soane Museum cannot, in Richardson's day, have been motivated by the thought of monetary gain. The price Soane had paid, though a substantial sum in 1833, works out for 8,625 drawings at little more than five old pence a sheet. The drawings for particular clients, discussed above, will hardly have been worth more than three or four shillings, while the value of Richardson's entire collection of Adam material cannot have exceeded a few pounds. In August 1863 when he disposed of 516 mixed architectural drawings, including many by Adam, to the Victoria and Albert Museum he received a sum of £35 so even after thirty years the price for English architectural drawings stood at no more than one shilling and two pence per sheet.

However he came by it, it is clear that Richardson formed his collection out of a genuine interest in his national architecture and in its history. His own publications prove him to have been a serious student of English sixteenth- and seventeenth-century architecture, and if he 'borrowed' drawings from Soane's office, or took them from the museum, he did so with the intention of studying them himself. It is also possible that he was motivated by a sense of grievance. On Soane's death he had hoped to be made an assistant curator and librarian at the museum but the trustees made no such appointment and, when his employment as Soane's clerk ceased, he was treated like any other visitor to the museum. After thirteen years' work for his master, who was elderly and almost blind, Richardson may well have salved his conscience with the notion that a modest study collection which he would use, even if it were formed with pickings from his master's office, was something to which he was morally entitled. At the end of his life he may even have felt that he paid back his 'borrowings' in spirit if not in fact. Both in practice and as an author he had served his profession well and, while he sold his Adam drawings and designs by Sir John Soane to the recently founded South Kensington Museum, he presented a sketch book of his own to the Soane Museum together with a collection of the drawings which he had used to illustrate the lectures he gave at Somerset House, while master of the architecture class in the school of design from 1845 to 1852.

Besides the designs for particular clients listed above, two other drawings in Richardson's collection may be demonstrated to have been in the Adam volumes. The Adam index mentions seven sheets of drawings for the archway at Hyde Park Corner and four drawings of unidentified bridge designs, all in volume 21. In each case the number of drawings in the Soane Museum is now one less than in the Adam index while one drawing of each subject has found its way into Richardson's collection.

That so many drawings may be demonstrated to have once been in the Adam collection at the Soane Museum provides an irreproachable provenance for many of the anonymous sketches that Richardson has inscribed as being by *Adam* or *Adams*. One pencil elevation of a colonnaded bridge (cat. 28) seems certainly to have been cut from one of the volumes of sketches and there are many gaps in volumes 54 and 55 which could be filled by drawings now in the Victoria and Albert Museum. Even the slightest pencil scribble can thus, if its style accords with similar visual notes in the Soane Museum, be accepted as an Adam drawing. On the other hand there are some designs which have clearly nothing to do with the brothers or their office beyond a generic similarity of subject or style to the work the Adams produced. We have no evidence how these designs were acquired. In so far as Richardson considered them to be by Adam they have some interest as documents in the history of architectural connoisseurship and on this account they are given a place in this catalogue under an 'Adamesque' category, though it is evident that Richardson at times allowed himself considerable licence in his use of the 'Adams' label.

Other drawings by Adam have, from time to time, been acquired by the museum by purchase. A large working elevation of the Porter's Lodge at Syon (cat. 110) is one of the earliest architectural drawings acquired by the museum and all four picturesque views in watercolour were bought at different dates. The museum has also acquired a number of anonymous eighteenth-century architectural drawings in Adam's manner (cat. 150–153) and a large collection of finished designs for chimneypieces (cat. 163–192), some of which purported to be by Adam when they were bought from the Brompton Road dealer, Mr E. Parsons in 1890. Mr Parsons is known to have bought material from C. J. Richardson and will probably have been familiar with his pencil inscriptions and some of the Adam drawings. At any event the chimney piece drawings which he acquired had, by the time they were sold to the museum, gained forged signatures of *R. Adam* which almost look as if the forger has mistaken Richardson's pencil note of authorship for an authentic signature and has set out to copy it. The drawings are also inscribed *Adelphi* and are given various spurious dates. No doubt these inscriptions were added because by 1890 an Adam revival was in progress in country house interior design rekindling interest in original designs by the architect. Two of the chimneypiece designs prove to be by Henry Holland (cat. 191, 192), and the rest are anonymous.

Mr Parsons's drawings are forgeries but only in the sense that they are not, as they pretend to be, by Robert Adam. The last drawing which must be mentioned here is a complete fake (cat. 197). It was purchased by the museum in 1938 and as it is copied from a plate in A. T. Bolton's *The Architecture of Robert and James Adam* published in 1922 must have been made some time after that. It is on a paper and in a style of draughtsmanship entirely unlike any other drawing associated with the brothers' work except for one lonely accomplice in deception which has now found its way into the Cooper-Hewitt in New York.

1 For a more detailed account of the business affairs of the brothers see Rowan 1974 II.

2 Professor Alan Tait has made a particular study of Robert Adam's picturesque drawings; for these see his two exhibition catalogues, Edinburgh 1972 and 1978. He is inclined to see a closer link between these drawings and real building projects though the evidence is not conclusive. See also Tait 1981.

3 When Adam returned to London in 1758 he brought with him two continental draughtsmen, L.B. Dewez from Liège and the Roman, Agostino Brunias. Dewez was to be his 'plan man and line drawer' while Brunias specialised in ornaments and figures. Robert also asked James to recruit draughtsmen in Scotland who could be trained in his manner. From this it is clear that the mechanical side of drawing was always delegated in the Adam office though references in letters to 'my way of drawing' make it clear that the final appearance of any design depended on Adam himself. For Brunias and Dewez *see* Fleming 1962, p. 216 and for Adam collaborators in general Stillman 1966, Chapter 4.

4 The first phrase is a famous jibe from Horace Walpole, writing in an anti-Adam mood to the Countess of Upper Ossory in 1785; the second comes from a remarkable and little known attack contained in the Appendix to James Peacock's *OIKIAIA or Nutshells* of 1785. Here Adam is lampooned as 'a wonderful genius', 'a certain compounder of ceilings' and an architect whose elevations have 'impassioned movement'.

5 See for example the popular *Practical House Carpenter*, 1788, or *The Builder's Sketch Book*, 1793.

6 For an account of the history of the Adam drawings between the deaths of the brothers and their arrival in the Soane Museum see Tait 1978 and Rowan 1985, pp. 10–12.

7 Some of Bailey's handlists survive stuck into the covers of individual volumes. Spiers's scrutiny of the volumes from which his catalogue was prepared is recorded in his diaries which remain in the Soane Museum.

8 The list of contents made by the Adam family is in the Scottish Record Office, Blair Adam Papers 4/25 (not, as stated by Tait, 4/197). The collation is as follows: in the Adam list Vol. 1 to Vol. 16 becomes Vol. 28 to Vol. 43 in the Soane Museum series except Vol. 10 which becomes Vol. 48; thereafter the sequences vary. Vol. 17 is Vol. 37, Vol. 18 is Vol. 45, Vol. 19 is Vol. 44, Vol. 20 is Vol. 46, Vol. 21 is Vol. 51 and Vols. 22 and 23 are Vol. 49 and 50.

9 Richardson's career as an assistant to Soane and his activities in building up his own collection is further discussed in the introduction to the volume by Pierre du Prey on the architectural drawings by Sir John Soane in the Victoria and Albert Museum, 1985. See also *The Dictionary of National Biography*: C.J. Richardson (1806–1871).

Note to the Reader

The drawings described here divide naturally into three broad categories: (i) architectural studies, sketches and free-hand designs; (ii) drawings relating to specific Adam commissions; and (iii) designs for individual features whose intended location is unknown. Within the first category the material, which is very varied, has been sub-divided to bring particular drawing types together as groups. These sub-divisions are as follows: Academic and Antique studies; Theoretical and Sketch designs; Picturesque drawings and Landscape compositions; and finally Sketch projects, that is designs for particular buildings which cannot be identified but which appear to be linked to real proposals rather than to theoretical schemes. In general terms this progression by sub-section tends to present a development from Adam's early to his more mature work, though it must be stressed that the progression is not absolute. The second category, drawings for identified commissions, is arranged alphabetically by place and all drawings related to a particular job, whether sketches, design or working drawings, details of individual rooms or of pieces of furniture are entered together under the same heading. The third category, covering drawings for unidentified schemes and unidentified individual features, is largely concerned with designs for furnishings and for chimneypieces.

All three categories, and particularly the first and the third, contain drawings which are clearly not by the Adam brothers nor from their office. The resemblance they bear to known Adam types varies. Some are close to the Adam style, either in subject matter or treatment, while others have only a vague similarity to recommend them. At some time however all were thought to be Adam drawings. They are included here both for completeness and for the opportunity they provide to set Adam and Adamesque side by side. In each category designs which are not by the brothers are placed after authentic drawings and follow the same subject groups.

Individual entries follow the pattern established by other catalogues of architectural drawings published by the museum. While most of this material will be self-explanatory, a note should perhaps be added on provenance, inscriptions and scale. A very large proportion of the Adam drawings in the museum come, as is noted above, from the collection of Charles James Richardson. Their acquisition is recorded in the museum's *Register of Drawings Vol. 3* and dates from 1863 when a mixed collection of 126 drawings was purchased for £25.0.0. to be followed perhaps some months later by an 'Architectural Album', made up by Richardson and purchased on 11 August the same year for a further £35.0.0. The accession numbers given to the loose drawings run from No. 3309 to 3435 (3337 appears to have been omitted) and include 126 sheets. Twelve of these are particularly noted in the Register as 'original designs by R. Adam'; the rest are not described. The album, which contained 512 drawings, had the single accession number 3436. The relevant entry in the Register is as follows: 'A collection of (512) Drawings and Sketches by R. Adam, Sir William Chambers, Flaxman, Gandy, Kent, Nash, Daniell, Cousins, Parke, Cipriani, Stothard, Soane, J. Wyatt, Vanbrugh and others (with four prints), collected by C. J. Richardson of whom purchased'. Though this album is now disbound many of the smaller drawings are still stuck to the backing paper where Richardson fixed them – on occasions several to one page – and often it is this old mounting that bears an inscription in Richardson's hand attributing the drawing to Adam. Sometimes both the drawing itself and the mount will be inscribed by Richardson who took at times rather too hopeful a view as to the authorship of some of the more modest drawings in his collection which, if it contained pilferings from the Soane Museum – whether his own or others – also found room for a considerable quantity of designs picked up elsewhere. In this catalogue where a drawing is clearly by Robert Adam, or from his office, I have not thought it necessary to record all of Richardson's inscriptions. On the other hand where a drawing is not by Adam but was thought by Richardson to be so the inscription is included.

Adam inscriptions pose a different problem. Both Robert and James have clearly identifiable signatures yet the evidence of the inscriptions on the Adam drawings in the Soane Museum is that many different clerks at different times identified and titled the office drawings. Inscriptions in an enterprise as large as the brothers' practice can offer little or no guide to the authenticity of a drawing. What may be worth recording however is the degree of care with which any drawing is noted: clearly the brothers imposed a certain house style – very much as a modern architect's office does today – and there is, for formal presentation or clients drawings, a certain bold cursive script which seems to be typical of the Adam office. Where this occurs it is described below as 'office copperplate'.

It was not until the end of the eighteenth century that fixed scale rules began to be used in building and engineering offices. Robert and James Adam do not appear to have used a scale rule for their normal office work and their drawings usually carry a drawn scale from which measurements can be taken. This scale does not normally vary within a single set of drawings but their is no standard scale or set of scales for Adam office drawings as a whole. Like their contemporaries in Mid-Georgian Britain, the Adams and their clerks fixed the scale for a drawing visually according to the size of the structure to be shown and the space available on a sheet of paper. This can result in a wide variety and in what, to our more systems-bound age, might appear as a series of exceedingly inconvenient scales, yet to men accustomed to reading a drawing with a pair of dividers to hand, the range of scales posed no problem. Adam scales can not however be reduced to the simple ratios of today – 1 to 500 or $\frac{1}{8}$th scale – and are recorded here in a more cumbersome way, as for example '$2\frac{1}{4}$ in. to 10 feet'.

List of Abbreviations

c.	Circa
cat.	Refers to the present catalogue
d.	Dated
Insc.	Inscribed
Lit.	Literature
(plate)	Plate in catalogue
repr.	Reproduced
RIBA	Royal Institute of British Architects
s.	Signed
SMD	Sir John Soane's Museum, Adam drawings
V&A	Victoria and Albert Museum
w/m	Watermark

Catalogue

The drawings are by Robert Adam or the Adam office, unless otherwise mentioned.

The entries are set out as follows:

Place (if place is not known, name of client or subject of drawing).

General note.

Description(s) of drawing(s). Inscriptions shown in italics. Unless otherwise mentioned inscriptions are on the drawing and in the medium of the drawing. Watermarks are mentioned only when dated. Measurements are of the sheet and expressed in millimetres, height before width.

Literature (including exhibitions). For details see the Select Bibliography.

Commentary. Inscriptions are shown in italics.

The catalogue also includes drawings by the following hands (for detailed listing see the Index):

Anonymous hands
Jacques Louis Clérisseau
Henry Holland
John Johnson
Daniel Robertson

PLATE I (cat. I)

Studies and Sketches

Academic and Antique Studies

CORINTHIAN CAPITAL AND ENTABLATURE

1 Academic elevation probably copied from an eighteenth-century edition of Vignola's *Regola delli cinque ordini d'archetettura*. c.1754. (pl.1).

Pen and ink and wash, heightened with white 247x200

3436.64

Prov.: C. J. Richardson.

The clumsy application of washes and the difference in handling between the crisp drawing of the acanthus leaves in the capital and the lax and awkward vegetable forms in the frieze, together with the pattern-book source of the design, suggest that this drawing is an early student exercise by Robert or James. The younger brother had marked theoretical interests – or pretensions – in later life but this seems an inadequate reason for attributing this design specifically to James Adam.

NEO-ANTIQUE COLUMN BASE

2 Finished rendered elevation of the base of a classical column, enriched with elaborate invented mouldings. Black ruled border. c.1755-57. (pl.2).

s.: in pencil *Robt Adam*.

Pen and ink and wash 349x510

3436.7

Prov.: C. J. Richardson.

Drawn to a large scale – the diameter of the column is 280 mm where it joins the base – this highly wrought design for the base of a column does not accord exactly with the established profiles of any of the five orders of the Renaissance. It is rather an Adam 'invented' order where the richness of the decorative overlay, particularly the 'new' motif of scallop shell and acanthus leaf on the upper torus moulding and the relief panel of Roman armour and martial trophies at the bottom, indicate the sense of liberation which the contact with real antiquity brought to Adam. Though anti-traditional the academic or theoretical nature of this study suggests that it may date from Robert's Roman years.

ANTIQUE FRAGMENTS

3 Picturesque composition of antique fragments in a landscape setting with ruins in the background.

Insc. *Original sketch by Robert Adam arct.*

Pen and ink, and wash heightened with white 423x355

3436.6

Prov.: C. J. Richardson.

Elements in this composition, such as the handling of the tree to the right of the group of fragments, the form of the centrally placed tripod, and the panel with a group of shields, are characteristic of Adam. Generally however the drawing is very poor and the application of the washes weak. Either this is a very early work in Rome or an esquisse by a clerk training in the Adam office.

PLATE 2 (cat. 2)

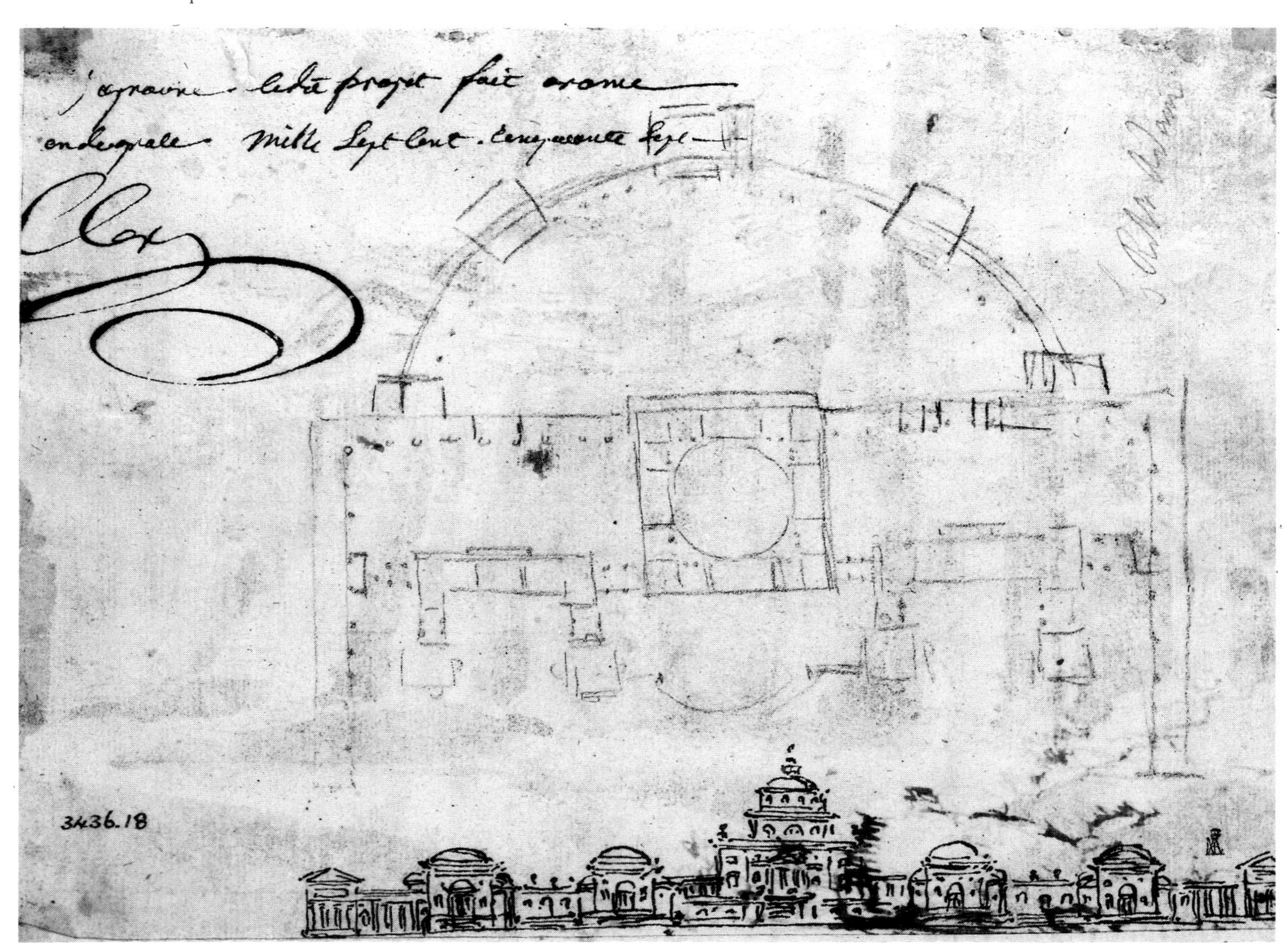

PLATE 3 (cat. 6)

THE ROTONDA IN THE VILLA DORIA PAMPHILI, ROME

4 Part elevation showing one round-headed archway, and one wall pier framed by unfluted Ionic pilasters with garlanded capitals. Arabesque panels on the pier are fully detailed with a classical figure in relief above the cornice at impost level. Sections of the panelling of the dome are also shown. *Verso* pencil plan of one quarter of the room.

Insc. *Stanza Rotonda nella Villa Pamphili* with an erased inscription above. Mount inscribed by Richardson *Robt Adams*, and *249* and on the *Verso*, partly erased, *Niche' con statue.*

Pencil and pen and ink with light washes 412x280

362.1885

Prov.: from C. J. Richardson's collection, purchased separately February 1885.

This drawing, which records an interior in the famous villa designed by Alessandro Algardi for Prince Camillo Pamfili in 1650, is not by Adam. Richardson may however be correct in suggesting a provenance through the Adam office as the type of architectural decoration recorded here was an essential element in the formation of Adam's own style. Adam is known to have collected record drawings of this sort which may have been prepared for him by Italian draughtsmen or purchased ready made during his Roman years.

SECTION OF A DOMED ROTUNDA

5 Sectional elevation of a circular room (or an apse) with paired Ionic pilasters round the walls, a continuous Doric entablature and irregular octagonal coffering arranged between broad ribs on the dome. Sectional details of the timber construction of the roof are shown.

Pen and ink and wash 244x220

3436.234

Prov.: C. J. Richardson.

This incomplete and not very competent drawing has the character more of a survey of an existing building than of an original architectural design. The decoration of the dome with its mixture of ribs which continue the lines of the pilasters and a coffered pattern behind them is Roman or Torinese in origin and appears in the work of Pietro da Cortona, Bernini, Carlo Fontana, Gallilei and Juvarra.

Theoretical and Sketch Designs

DESIGN FOR A ROYAL PALACE OR PUBLIC BUILDING

6 Plan and principal elevation. A centrally-planned three-storey structure, domed and contained in a square building, is flanked by U-shaped courts on either side each with twin centrally-planned domed pavilions, and a long, low wing ending in a pedimented temple front beyond. A semi-circular court with interval blocks extends across the entire back of the building. (pl. 3).

Insc. In the hand of J. L. Clérisseau *j'aprouve cette project fait a rome an de grace Mille Sept Cent Cinquante Sept – Cler.* and in Richardson's hand *by Robt Adam* and *Robt Adam 36*.

Pencil, pen and ink and sepia wash 192x255

3436.18 (*recto*)

Prov.: C. J. Richardson.

Linked possibly to Adam's ideal schemes for the rebuilding of Lisbon this first sketch of an idea for a Royal Palace (which his mentor Clérisseau signs with a flamboyant note of approval) bears evident traces of the influence of Roman Neo-classicism and of the French Academy. The centrally-planned principal structure, the sense of weight, the dome profiles and the Palladian connotations of the enclosing outer wings all suggest that Adam, at 29, and nearing the end of his stay in Rome, had mastered an international Neo-classical idiom that Giacomo Quarenghi was later to employ. A dome with niched drum, similar to that suggested on the main block here, appears in Adam's sketches in the Soane Museum S.M.D. Vol. 2, No. 94. For the *verso* see cat. 15.

A RUINED ANTIQUE SHRINE

7 Freehand sketch showing, in sectional elevation, a vaulted Roman interior; *Verso* a rapid sketch plan showing in diagrammatic form the Piazza del Popolo, Rome, with its two churches at the end of converging streets and (?) the course of the Tiber. c.1757. (pl. 4).

Insc. In Adam's hand *Une cote du Temple Ruiné et restoré avec les fragmens antiques.*

Pen and ink on this paper 237x190 (irregular)

3436.60

Prov.: C. J. Richardson.

This vaulted chapel fuses English Palladian models – the Diocletian window and Kentian chimneypiece – with the sort of assemblage of Antiquities popular with connoisseurs and dealers in mid-century Rome. Very much the taste of a young man, this free admixture of elements – the large bucrania and anthemion motif in the frieze, the relief 'fan' behind the chimneypiece, and the Roman house altar which Adam incorporates into the transom of the chimneypiece – indicates even before the architect's return to Britain the free treatment of sources and anti-academic approach that he was to propose in matters of architectural design.

A RUINED TEMPLE CONVERTED FOR CHRISTIAN USE

8 Freehand sketch showing, in sectional elevation, the end elevation of a vaulted interior with an altar flanked by niches. *Verso* brush smudges in grey wash. (pl. 5).

Insc. In Adam's hand *Un autre temple frequente par un Hermit et par [ou il et converté a] Chappelle;* The inscription within square brackets is crossed out and corrected, in Clérisseau's(?) hand, to read *e par lui changé en Chappelle*

Pen and sepia ink on thin paper 216x186

3436.59

Prov.: C. J. Richardson.

This rapid sketch done in Rome, and encapsulating the architect's essentially romantic approach to much of Antiquity was, with cat. 7, to be used later as the basis for an elaborate design for a proposed classical ruin at Kedleston in Derbyshire (see cat. 61).

PLATE 4 (cat. 7)

PLATE 5 (cat. 8)

PLATE 6 (cat. 9)

DESIGN FOR A PUBLIC BUILDING

9 Sketch plan and principal elevation. A square main block with central circular domed area is flanked, front and rear, by short wings which enclose side courts that end in a columnar screen. The elevation proposes a giant order of columns across a central segmental recess as the principal feature of the main block with single flanking aedicules and sculptural panels above. Alternative elevations for the wings show, on the right, a block as high as the central building with an external coffered apse screened by columns and, left, a lower colonnaded structure with statues in niches at either end. (pl. 6).

Insc. by C. J. Richardson *Adams*.

Pen and sepia ink 170x265

3436.54

Prov.: C. J. Richardson.

This ideal scheme appears to date from Adam's Roman period. Though many of the elements investigated here were to reappear in executed work in Britain, for example the duality of two scales of columns which appears at the garden front of Stowe or the exterior apse in the wings which Adam used as late as his work at Balbardie, other features did not appear in executed designs. The principal element which was to remain on paper only is the exceptionally shallow, almost quattrocento style dome and drum, which may be noted among the architect's sketches of the late 1750s. Comparable designs in the Soane Museum are S.M.D., Vol. 9, Nos. 68, 159, 167 and 209.

A COLUMNAR FAÇADE

10 Study sketch of a three-bay façade articulated by a giant order of Greek Ionic pilasters supporting a continuous entablature. A minor Doric order interpenetrates the Ionic pilasters and is expressed in the middle bay as a Doric aedicular porch with triglyph frieze and pediment. The side bays appear to be open as in a loggia.

Insc. by C. J. Richardson *Adams*.

Pencil 165x265

3436.53

Prov.: C. J. Richardson.

This light study on an old theme, that goes back through Vanbrugh and Inigo Jones to Michelangelo, bears in its proportions an indelible Adam character. The shallow pitch of the central pediment, the switch from a triglyph frieze to an invented pattern in the outer bays, and the long low rectangles above this frieze are all characteristic of the architect's work in the early 1770s. Adam's use of such a system of interpenetrating orders is illustrated in schemes for a triumphal arch and screen at Hyde Park Corner, S.M.D., Vol. 51, No. 77, and, on a different scale, in the gallery at Syon, see cat. 111.

A TRIUMPHAL ARCH

11 Part elevation of a routine study showing a round-headed arch flanked by single narrow bays framed by thin Doric pilasters. *Verso* Light sketch of a ruined arch in a landscape with sarcophagus and stream.

Pencil 210x296

3436.8

Prov.: C. J. Richardson.

DESIGN FOR A COVED CEILING

12 Sketch plan and part section of a ceiling for a small square room. The cove is decorated with drapery swags, with bows in each corner and oval patera between. The flat of the ceiling is a large Greek cross, defined by a Greek key border, with small classical figures placed diagonally in each corner and a roundel of a putto riding a dolphin in the centre of the cross.

Pen and ink and grey wash 240x182

9110.B

Prov.: R. Jackson, 1883.

The distinctly architectural, and archaeological, character of this ceiling would place the design early in Adam's career, either in the Roman period or soon after.

Picturesque Compositions

SANTA TRINITÀ DEI MONTI, ROME

13 Perspective sketch looking across tiled roofs to the twin campanile of the church. The *verso* of cat. 155. c.1755.

Insc. *Back of Trinità dei Monti, Rome – View towards Monte Mario.*

Pencil and wash 197x205

3436.47 (*verso*)

Prov.: C. J. Richardson.

This celebrated sixteenth-century church at the top of the Spanish Steps will have been particularly familiar to Robert Adam whose lodgings for the whole of his stay in Rome were in the Casa Guarnieri in the Piazza di Spagna at the bottom of the same steps.

THE TEMPLE OF AESCULAPIUS, SPALATO

14 Perspective view of the partially ruined front of the temple with two Corinthian antae pilasters and a richly moulded doorcase. Morning sunlight washes the long east side of the building, illuminating a group of figures in the right foreground, a man walking up the temple steps and a boy leading a horse round a large sarcophagus on the far side of the building. 1757. (pl. 7).

Pen and ink with grey washes 255x365

3436.10

Prov.: C. J. Richardson.

This soft and delicately washed drawing was to be engraved by Francesco Bartolozzi in Venice and published as the second of two perspective views of the temple at Diocletian's palace at Split, Yugoslavia (Plate 42) in Adam's *Ruins of the Palace of the Emperor Diocletian at Spalatro* of 1764. In the engraved plate (pl. 8), which is the same size as this drawing, Bartolozzi considerably increases the amount of architectural detail that is recorded, no doubt on the basis of other drawings of the temple also published in Adam's volume. Adam's visit to Split, then known by its Italian name Spalato (spelled by Adam Spalatro), lasted from 22 July to 28 August 1757. The team of artists who accomplished the survey of the ruins was four: Adam himself, J. L. Clérisseau, Agostino Brunias and Laurent-Benôit Dewez. Of this group it was Clérisseau who was responsible for drawing perspective views of the ruins and this design with its strong chiaroscuro, bold shadow lines and broadly handled foliage is characteristic of his work. For an account of Adam's visit to Split and his choice of draughtsmen see Fleming 1958 and 1962, pp. 216, 235–40.

COMPOSITION OF ROMAN RUINS

15 Perspective, freehand sketch of classical buildings, including a flight of steps, a Corinthian colonnade and a portico, built against a steep embankment. (pl. 9).

Verso d. 1757. (See cat. 6).

Insc. by C. J. Richardson on mount *by Robt Adam* and *34* and *38*.

Pen and sepia ink with grey wash 191x255 (irregular, the sheet trimmed)

3436.18

Prov.: C. J. Richardson.

The crude buttresses which interrupt the architecture in this view, its incoherent character and, more particularly, the top of the circular tower beside the portico which would not in reality fit in, establish this sketch as a pure architectural fantasy in which Adam is perhaps responding to the massy effects of sub-structures on the Palatine and at Tivoli. Compositions of this character were later to be proposed quite frequently as pictorial elements in decorative schemes as in the dining room and first proposals for the entrance hall at Osterley (see cat. 88 and 91).

COMPOSITION OF ROMAN RUINS WITH FIGURES AND TOMBS

16 Perspective freehand sketch of a ruined vaulted structure with a monumental sarcophagus tomb with a recumbent effigy and foliage in the foreground.

Insc. on the mount by C. J. Richardson *Robt Adam.*

Pen and sepia ink 200x265

3436.17

Prov.: C. J. Richardson.

The free and confident character of the draughtsmanship in this sketch fully supports Richardson's attribution to Robert Adam.

PLATE 7 (cat. 14)

PLATE 8

PLATE 9 (cat. 15)

CLASSICAL LANDSCAPE WITH A RIVER AND TEMPLES

17 A view by a river bank with a circular arcaded temple, part of a bridge, and a tetrastyle portico appearing through the trees on the far side. A herdsman with cattle is in the foreground and figures sit in boats on the river. *Verso* light sketch of landscaped park with a domed rotunda on a hill, stables to the right and the portico of a country house to the left. (pl. 10, *recto*).

Insc. on the mount by Richardson *Adams* and *278*.

Pen and ink and pencil, the *verso* pencil 200 x 310

3436.50

Prov.: C. J. Richardson.

Though slight the sylvan sketches on both sides of this sheet have a deftness and elegance that make Adam's authorship most probable.

SKETCH OF A RUINED ROMAN EXEDRA

18 A large sarcophagus is shown in elevation against a curving exedra with a regular succession of niches, free-standing columns and salient entablatures surmounted by statues. *Verso* similar but very faint composition.

Pencil 222 x 283

3436.9

Prov.: C. J. Richardson.

This drawing, which is very slight, could be by Adam. Richardson makes no attribution for it.

VIEW OF A RUINED ROMAN INTERIOR

19 A hemi-cycle, with deep recesses screened by columns like the Pantheon and partly vaulted, end in a straight wall. Figures sit or stand in the foreground and foliage is seen above the opening in the vault. For the *Verso* see cat.20

Insc. twice by C. J. Richardson *R. Adams*.

Pen and ink, pencil and grey wash 164 x 177

3436.16 (*recto*)

Prov.: C. J. Richardson.

Both the architecture and the draughtsmanship of this drawing are crude and ill considered. If it is by Adam – and the quality of the brush drawing on the *verso* suggests a better provenance than this design – it may be presumed to be an early student work.

IDEAL LANDSCAPE WITH CLASSICAL BUILDINGS AND RUINS

20 An imaginary view in free wash, perhaps of the forum, with the columns of a temple on the right, a large umbrella pine in the centre and a portico, rotunda and tall block seen in shade on the left. For the *recto* see cat. 19

Wash 164 x 177

3436.16 (*verso*)

Prov.: C. J. Richardson.

PLATE 10 (cat. 17)

CLASSICAL BATH WITH FEMALE FIGURES

21 A corner of a large open bath-house, with a screen of Ionic columns on the left and an arch, inside which a statue of a girl with a putto is set on a high plinth. Water issues from a mask on the plinth into the bath.

Insc. In C. J. Richardson's hand *Rt Adam* and *263*.

Pen and ink with watercolour 157x122

3436.15

Prov.: C. J. Richardson.

Despite Richardson's inscription this weak drawing is not by Adam and is unlikely ever to have been in the brothers' collection of drawings.

CLASSICAL RUIN COMPOSITION INCLUDING THE PANTHEON

22 Outline drawing partially completed with washes and colour showing the back of the Pantheon on the left with an assemblage of ruined brick walls and part of a vaulted interior on the right.

w/m: J. Whatman 1794

Pen and ink with water-colour 192x434

3436.19

Prov.: C. J. Richardson.

Inscriptions on plaques on the buildings and beneath a monument in the interior appear to be inventions. One could refer to Caius Pescennius Niger, Commander in Syria who opposed Septimius Severus for the Empire. The date of the watermark makes any attribution to Adam impossible.

ROMAN RUIN COMPOSITION

23 Outline perspective view of a pedimented archway, like Chamber's ruined arch at Kew, with a domed building beyond and a pair of Doric columns and a niche in the foreground. Various freely drawn figures. *Verso*: vague sketch of a triumphal arch.

Insc. on a plaque below the pediment of the arch *DAN^{L} ROBERTS^{n} FECIT.*

Pen and ink over pencil 227x275

3436.52

Prov.: C. J. Richardson.

Daniel Robertson, the author of this design, was a relative of Robert and James Adam. Though much younger he may have trained with them and was a partner of William Adam in London from 1799 to 1801. He died in Ireland after 1843.

Late Romantic Landscapes

LANDSCAPE WITH FIGURES CROSSING A BRIDGE

24 An evening scene by a pool and waterfall, all in shadow with figures in the foreground beside an Italianate hut. Trees on the left by the bridge are silhouetted against the evening light which catches the side of a mountain with vestiges of a castle set high above the bridge. Theatrical in character and broadly handled with thick pen lines and dark, summary washes of ochre, grey, blue and brown.

Pencil, pen and ink with water-colour 303x507

P.3–1938

Lit. and repr.: Edinburgh 1972, pl. 22.

PLATE 11 (cat. 25)

PLATE 12 (cat. 26)

A CASTLE ON A CLIFF

25 A massive and partly ruinous castle, with a substantial round tower is caught in a beam of sunlight above a densely wooded ravine with a river at its base. Two figures of fishermen are in the foreground and trees and woodland fill the left hand half of the composition. (pl. 11).

Pen and ink with water-colour 248 x 315

D.1894–1889

Prov.: Purchased from Mr. R. Jackson, 30 September 1889.

A HILLTOP CASTLE BY A LAKE

26 A roadway crossing the foreground of the composition from right to left zigzags uphill to a fortified gateway and towers on the top of a crag. At its base lies a long broad lake with the outline of a village on the farther bank and mountainous escarpments beyond. 1784. (pl. 12).

w/m: T. French

Dated *1784*.

Pen and sepia ink with coloured washes in blue, grey, biscuit and tan 203 x 322

130.1890

Prov.: Purchased in London by J. Percy from a Mr Danile, 13 December 1873. Sold to Messrs Vokins (Christie's, Percy sale, 15 April, 1890, lot 1) who sold it to the museum in 1890. A note on the mount by Percy reads 'on another drawing which D. had, of the same dimensions & certainly by the same hand was written 'Robert Adam Archt (Sic), Delin 1784': I did not purchase the latter because it was much injured by rubbing and was inferior to this'.

Lit: V & A 1927, pl. 2; Williams 1952, pl. 131.

This beautiful drawing, one of Robert Adam's most attractive landscape compositions, is far removed from the routine mechanisms of many of his exercises in this idiom. The arrangement of the composition, with its evocative glassy lake and sun drenched distances, is reminiscent of Claude's mature work of the 1650s and 1660s where the centre of interest stands on its own without the earlier props of trees or cliffs to left and right to frame the view.

MOUNTAINOUS LANDSCAPE WITH FIGURES

27 In the right foreground two women and a child in Classical dress sit below trees. The entrance to a tunnel is behind them. In front are the tumbling waters of a mountain torrent emptying from the mirror-like surface of a lake which is seen through a fold in the hills. A ruined castle with a bridge and a low round tower is built beside the lake with mountains and wooded slopes rising behind it. 1774.

Verso dated in pencil *1774*.

w/m: T. Budgen

Pen and sepia ink with washes and water-colour 200 x 311

334–1872

Prov.: Hogarth & Sons, Mount St.

Three of these landscape compositions (cat. 24–26) are discussed by Professor Alan Tait in Edinburgh 1972, nos. 56, 37 and 28. Here he attributes the most broadly handled drawings to James Adam, including cat. 24 above though, on the basis of the figures fishing in the foreground, he reserves cat. 25 to Robert.

Sketch Designs for Unidentified Buildings

DESIGN FOR A COLONNADED BRIDGE

28 Sketch elevation of part of a bridge on three arches. The central arch is segmental and spans 100 ft, the outer arches are each semi-circular and span 50 ft. The spandrels have large paterae and the entablature, at the level of the road, is decorated in the centre with a Vitruvian scroll frieze. The piers to the central arch are half octagons and support domed terminals to a Tuscan colonnade that extends across the whole of the middle span. The centre is filled by a pavilion with a loggia that overlooks the river. *Verso* sketches of foliage. (pl. 13).

PLATE 13 (cat. 28)

PLATE 14 (cat. 29)

Insc. with heights and spans, and on the mount by Richardson *Sketch by Adams*.

Pencil (cut down, the top corners trimmed) 108x278

3436.20

Prov.: C. J. Richardson.

A plan, which matches the design of this elevation and may be described as its companion drawing is in S.M.D. Vol. 9, No. 93. This is one of the volumes partly compiled by Adam himself and the drawing was No. 21 in Adam's catalogue of 'Sketches of bridges done in England since January 1758'. It seems likely that the elevation, here discussed, was at one stage No. 22 in Adam's list as a sheet has evidently been torn out of the volume after No. 21. There is no evidence to connect this bridge design with any particular project: its position amongst Adam's sketches suggests that it is too early to be connected with the Pulteney Bridge in Bath. A colonnaded bridge is, in any case, a recurrent theme in the architect's imagination with a pedigree going back through Vanbrugh to Palladio and Roman antiquity.

DESIGN FOR A RUSTIC BRIDGE

29 Large scale pictorial elevation in a landscape setting. A rusticated semi-circular arch flanked by polygonal piers with blank niches, and a second arch and niche on dry ground to the right. Semi-ruined with wooden paling to patch the parapet. A bold and generalised brush drawing. (pl. 14)

Insc. on *verso* partly erased, *November 93, The Bridge for Bl...*

Wash with water-colour 293x480

3436.22

Prov.: C. J. Richardson.

Though comparatively crude, freehand wash drawings of this character seem to have been used by Adam from time to time to develop ideas for picturesque or wood architecture whose primary function was to serve as a pictorial element in a park or landscape. Bridges such as those proposed for David Garrick at Hendon (cf cat. 74) or for Bowood may well have passed through a stage similar to that recorded here.

SKETCH OF A THATCHED COUNTRY LODGE

30 Freehand elevation, in an imaginary landscape setting, of a circular two-storey lodge, with adjoining single-bay circular wings all with individual conical thatched roofs. Rustic Doric door case. (pl. 15).

Pen and sepia ink on pinkish brown paper 203x254

3436.35

Prov.: C. J. Richardson.

This dashing drawing penned on a surface which appears to be like blotting paper (with one large blot and traces of some numbers – '229.10' and '918.6' – in the hatching in the sky) illustrates an Adam tendency to develop an idea with whatever materials are immediately to hand. The plan of the lodge, a circle flanked by single-cell circular wings – perhaps there are four – suggests the type of ideal Neo-Renaissance planning that became a common starting point in many Adam schemes for garden buildings or other minor works. This sketch has some similarity to Adam's design for Tullysoul proposed for James McPherson about 1788 (S.M.D. Vol. 46, No. 7, Rowan 1985, pl. 1).

PLATE 15 (cat. 30)

DESIGN FOR A RUSTIC BUILDING IN A PARK

31 Sketch elevation of a symmetrical, single-storey building with thatched roofs, exaggerated rustic quoins and lattice windows. Five bays, with half-hipped gable ends and a dominant gabled centre bay. A rusticated arch, contains a Venetian window and a clock turret (or dovecote) above. (pl. 16).

Insc. by Richardson *Adams*.

Pencil and sepia ink, irregular 93 x 150

3436.24

Prov.: C. J. Richardson.

This rapid small sketch – little more than a scribble – records in a vigorous way a typical Adam method of architectural composition with its centre, links and separate ends all clearly distinguished. Its style is characteristic of many proposals for rustic lodges, cottages or farm buildings from the 1770s (cf. designs for the Duke of Bolton, the Earl of Harborough, Lord Wemyss, Mr Dalzell and Samuel Smith). The symmetry and official character of this elevation suggest that the building was intended for some specific use on an estate, such as a dairy, menagerie, or kennels, and that the rustic Venetian doorcase in the centre would be used by genteel visitors as well as by the inhabitants of the cottage lodges.

Sketch Designs of Architectural Details

DESIGN FOR A CAPITAL

32 Elevation of a pilaster shaft with a reversed ram's-head capital, the horns forming Ionic type volutes. The pilaster panelled with beaded edge and foliage. Pencil indication of entablature above.

Insc. by Richardson *Adam's*.

Pen and sepia ink over pencil, irregular 253 x 130

3436.42

Prov.: C. J. Richardson.

DESIGN FOR ARABESQUE PANELS WITH FIGURE TRIPODS

33 Sketch elevation of two tall panels in recessed frames: in one a male figures standing on a circular pedestal holds up a wide drum with a vase on dolphin supporters and anthemion above; in the other a tripod, decorated with lion masks at the top, supports a wide vase held up by two female figures, with swans above and an anthemion finial set against floral garlands and a wreath.

Pen and ink with grey wash, irregular 247 x 175

3436.40

Prov.: C. J. Richardson.

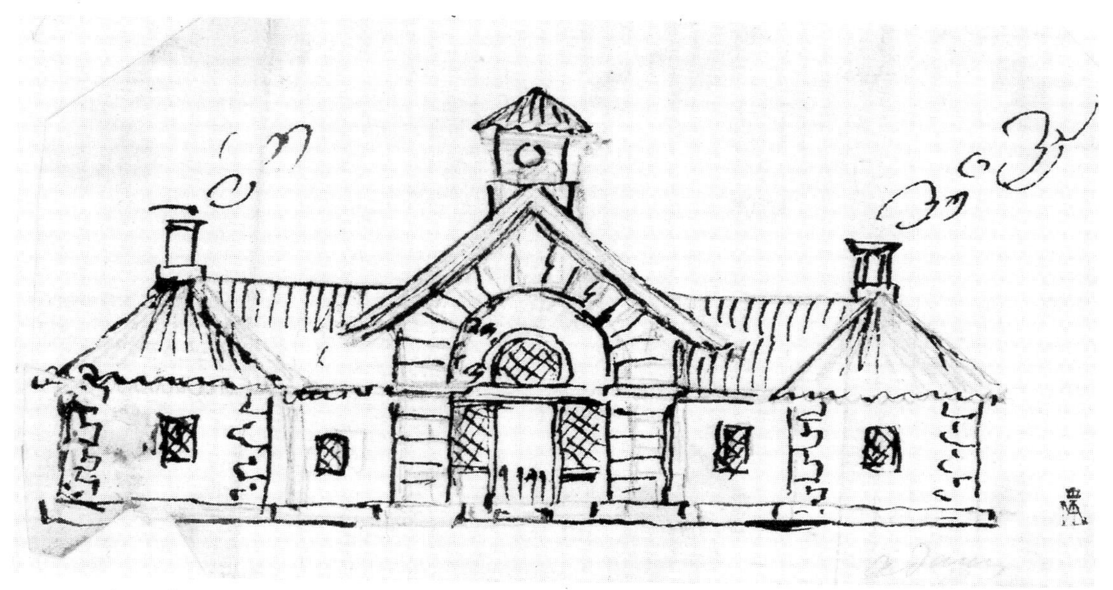

PLATE 16 (cat. 31)

DESIGN FOR PLASTERWORK DECORATION ON A WALL

34 A tall repeat pattern. Round plaques of figures surmounted by tapering panels alternate with urns on tripod bases with a garland loop dropping from the urns in a semi-circular border below each figure plaque. Paterae and bows continue the line of the tapering panels with swags hanging between the bows as a counterpoint to the garlands of the lower level.

Insc. in pencil *Robt Adam.*

Pen and sepia ink 88 x 70

3436.43

Prov.: C. J. Richardson.

DESIGNS FOR PLASTERWORK CEILING DECORATIONS

35 Freehand sketches for arabesques in plasterwork including two outline patterns for rectangular ceilings, an elaborate arrangement for repeat all-over wall patterning and two details of large symmetrical arabesque motifs, one of which – to the left of the sheet – is possibly a proposal for the decoration of the corner of a coved ceiling. *Verso* two plans for square ceilings and two patterns of arabesque arcades probably for the sides of a coved ceiling. (pl. 17).

Insc. by Richardson *Robt Adam.*

Pencil, partly overdrawn in pen and sepia ink, top corners trimmed 319 x 392

3436.39

Prov.: C. J. Richardson.

This unusually interesting sheet of sketch ideas shows, in one folio, Adam's design processes from rough skeletal schemes for the over-all pattern of a ceiling to the more intricate development of individual sections of detailed pattern. A range of characters between free arabesque work on an open field and more restricted geometrical panelling is also suggested here. The drawing style seems comparable to that in the sketch for the Osterley Etruscan room (see cat. 101 below) and this design may be dated to the early 1770s. A coved ceiling with arabesque arcades similar to those proposed here was executed for the Earl of Bective at Headfort House, Kells, Co. Meath about 1772.

TWO DESIGNS FOR FRIEZES

36 Rapid sketch designs of experimental character. A frieze mixing formal architectural motifs with common garden flowers above a second frieze of swans facing each other across rushes and plants.

Insc. in an eighteenth-century hand *frise*[sic] *for a Building by the Side of a River* and later in pencil *Robert Adam.*

Pen and ink, irregular 123 x 198

3436.44

Prov.: C. J. Richardson.

MEASURED SKETCH OF A DOOR HEAD

37 A slender console bracket with frieze block and cornice above. Also part of a frieze alternating anthemia and shells. For the *Verso* of this sheet see cat. 161.

Insc. with detailed measurements.

Pen and ink, irregularly trimmed 165 x 118

3436.23 (*recto*)

Prov.: C. J. Richardson.

PLATE 17 (cat. 35)

Sketch Designs for Tombs and Wall Monuments

DESIGN FOR A SARCOPHAGUS

38 The sarcophagus is set against a broad truncated pyramid, with an arch cut into it containing a rectangular relief sculpture and flanking statues. Short columns with trophies at their base flank the cörners of the pyramid.

Insc. by Richardson *Adams.*

Pencil 106x123

3436.25

Prov.: C. J. Richardson.

Alternative versions of this design exist in the volume of miscellaneous sketches by Adam, S.M.D., Vol. 54, Series 2, Nos 1 and 12. Mausolea with pyramids and funerary columns also appear in S.M.D., Vol. 2, Nos 1, 3 and 6.

DESIGN FOR A WALL MONUMENT

39 A break-front tablet with an obelisk above and a portrait bust. All very lightly indicated.

Insc. *392.*

Pencil, irregular 115x61

3436.27

Prov.: C. J. Richardson.

DESIGN FOR THE TOP OF A WALL MONUMENT

40 Sketch of a truncated pediment with quarter circle acroterion blocks and an urn at the top. Reclining figures on each slope of the pediment. Small scale.

Insc. by Richardson *Adams.*

Pencil, irregular with corners trimmed 100x121

3436.37

Prov.: C. J. Richardson.

PLATE 18 (cat. 42)

DESIGN FOR PSEUDO ANTIQUE PANEL DECORATION

41 Sketch for a sculpturesque plasterwork composition. A memorial tablet decorated with fasces and supported by griffons is surmounted by a large semi-circular panel of relief sculpture framed by an architrave with garlands below and tendril arabesques above with large birds perched upon them. A pelmet of three fan draperies at the top.

Insc. by Richardson *Adams.*

Pencil, corners trimmed 237 x 186

3436.38

Prov.: C. J. Richardson.

Though slight, the soft, easy style of these four sketches have absolute confidence and, on account of their provenance, may be accepted as autograph designs by Robert Adam.

Unidentified Sketch Designs by Different Hands

Drawings of sketch proposals for various buildings or details (on 9 sheets) said, by C. J. Richardson, to be by Robert Adam though clearly by different and inferior hands.

DESIGN FOR A PUBLIC LAVATORY

42 Perspective sketch of an oval building with triumphal arch entrance from which flanking Corinthian quadrants lead to terminal piers with niches and statues on the blocking course. A frieze of sculpture is suggested above the entrance arch which dwarfs two tiny figures standing below it. *Verso* sketch of a dome with swagged parapet. (pl. 18, *recto*).

Insc. *Design for a public Privy* and by Richardson *Robt Adams.*

Pen and ink, and wash over pencil 156 x 192

3436.11

Prov.: C. J. Richardson.

Neither the draughtsmanship, the architecture nor the coarse, earthy humour of this drawing bears any relationship to Robert Adam. The design is most probably a sketch for a cartoon lampooning, with lavatorial humour, both the inflated scale and didactic character of European architecture (and even more of architectural projects) after 1800. Hence this dedication of an heroic and truly gargantuan structure to what? A Regency public lavatory – and one which in truly neo-classical fashion envisages the evacuation of the bowels as a congregational activity with tiers of seats inside the oval rotunda. On top of this the didactic message of sculpture, such an element in contemporary architectural thought, is hammered home with all the verve (and all the crudity) of Gillray or Rowlandson at their most basic: the figures above the terminal piers – a man on the left and woman on the right – crouch down and having enormous buttocks relieve themselves over the cornice edge despite the gesticulations of figures waving wildly from the niches underneath. The arch before the 'privy' has a phallic silhouette and in the frieze above it a coach has stopped with crouching figures on the left and two men pissing on the right. There is something a little adolescent in all this, as if a student were making fun of his masters and – if this is so – the lively little sketch of a dome on the back of drawing suggests that he had flair and perhaps a little knowledge of French fashions.

SKETCH FOR A GARDEN FORT

43 Sketch elevation of a symmetrical garden castle possibly intended as a screen for farm buildings. A gently bowed centre with five gun embrasures, battlements and corner bartizans is surmounted by a low second storey, three windows wide also with battlements and bartizans and with a central flag pole. The centre is flanked by battlemented gothic gateways with crossed arrow loops on either side and obliquely angled bastions with half round projections at either end of the elevation. (pl. 19).

Insc. in pencil *Design for an ornamental castle in a landscape Robt Adam.*

Pen and ink and grey wash 110x280

3436.13

Prov.: C. J. Richardson.

This light-hearted proposal for a folly screen may be compared with designs for forts for many eighteenth-century country estates. The genre is one to which Robert Adam made a very particular contribution but the idiom of this design is not his. Adam's castles do not employ the mixture of elements shown here: an artillery fort with pieces of ordnance, seventeenth-century bartizans and breastworks with medieval portcullis gates and arrow slits. Nor did he use gothic arches of this form in any new designs. The extended elevation and low silhouette of the fort might be compared with Lord Byron's castles by the lake of Newstead Abbey, to James Paine's work at Raby Home Farm, Co. Durham or the anonymous designs for castles at Wallington, Northumberland all dating from about the middle of the century.

DESIGN FOR A ROTUNDA FOR FIREWORKS

44 Elevation of a conventional Ionic rotunda raised on a square, stepped podium with lateral pedestals bearing the letters G and C. A central statue and crown finial to the dome.

Insc. *Robt Adams design for an illumination.*

Pen and ink and wash 104x93

3436.34

Prov.: C. J. Richardson.

This modest little temple most probably relates to a royal jubilee, perhaps that of the marriage of King George III and Queen Charlotte in 1786 as indicated by the crown and initial letters of the monarchs. It can hardly be a royal work. Adam had made designs for an illumination in the grounds of Buckingham House for the King's birthday in June 1763 (Adam 1773, Vol. I, No. 5, Pl. V) and later for the Earl of Hopetoun and for Sir Charles Frederick (S.M.D., Vol. 49, No. 1, 65 and 66). It was no doubt his knowledge of the published design that led Richardson to attribute this drawing to the architect.

DESIGN FOR A CARYATID LOGGIA FOR FIREWORKS

45 Sketch elevation of a loggia of four garlanded caryatids with an elaborate attic above, which acts as a plinth for a group of three figures. Sockets for illuminations are set along both the main cornices.

Pen and ink and grey wash with water-colour 104x81

3436.33

Prov.: C. J. Richardson.

This loggia was no doubt intended for the same occasion as cat. 44 above and is by the same designer.

DESIGN FOR AN ANTIQUE FRIEZE

46 Acanthus and foliage tendrils symmetrically arranged about central female mask. A student design?

Pencil 35x162

3436.30

Prov.: C. J. Richardson.

SKETCH OF AN ARCHITECTURAL WALL MONUMENT

47 Sketch elevation of an Ionic aedicule framing an urn and set above a long sarcophagus. A student exercise?

Water-colour over pencil 98x62

3436.32

Prov.: C. J. Richardson.

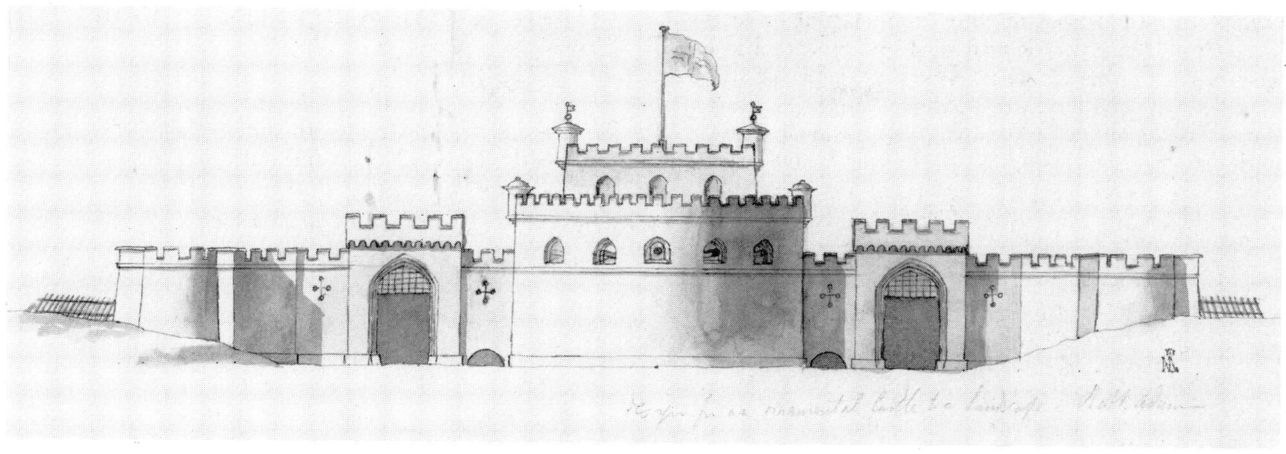

PLATE 19 (cat. 43)

ANTIQUE STUDY

48 Perspective sketch of a Corithinian capital with a ruined entablature. A student exercise?

Water-colour 122x76

3436.31

Prov.: C. J. Richardson.

DESIGN FOR A GOTHICK ORGAN CASE

49 Free hand sketch elevation. A high pitched gable with stepped clustered pipes to form a corner 'turret' and an open central area for the pipes framed by a wide cusped arch. The lower case solid with a smaller version of the gabled front in the centre for a clock.

Insc. twice by Richardson *Adams.*

Pen and ink over pencil 228x140

3436.63

Prov.: C. J. Richardson.

This drawing though superficially reminiscent of Adam Gothick is not in Adam's hand. The scratchy drawing and varied nib width has no parallel in his work while the sort of Gothic that is here revived is more in keeping with the taste of about 1820 than 30 or 40 years before.

A PAIR OF SPHINX GATE PIERS

50 Detailed outline elevation of the top of two gate piers showing an astragal, main cornice and blocking course with free hand drawings of a pair of sphinxes whose heads, usually, are those of fashionable women with tête de mouton hairstyles and tilted hats.

Insc. on the back in a nineteenth-century hand *By Mr. Adams on the Gates of Sion House or are these the figures mentioned by Walpole at Versailles?*

Pen and ink 215x333

3436.62

Prov.: C. J. Richardson.

The free hand drawing here is poor and the bodies of the sphinxes are not of the Adam type whose front paws stretch out much further and who have always ample breasts.

PERSPECTIVE VIEW OF A RUSTIC STONE COTTAGE

51 A long, low, thatched cottage with a primitive stone portal of Druidical character flanked by a simple window on each side and Pylon-like chimneys. Set in a wood.

Insc. in Richardson's hand *Adams.*

Pencil, corners trimmed 114x202

3436.26

Prov.: C. J. Richardson.

Despite the inscription by Richardson neither the design of this cottage, nor the style of pencil draughtsmanship which is characteristic of an early 1800s date can be accepted as having any connection with Robert Adam.

Identified Designs

PLATE 20 (cat. 52)

BOWOOD, Wiltshire

Design for a ceiling, 1763.

52 Plan of a coved ceiling, with a rectangular centre framed by a double guilloche border. Both the coved and flat areas are filled with oval coffers framed by elaborate late rococo scrolls of foliage. (pl. 20).

Pen and ink and wash 286 x 266

9110A

Prov.: R. Jackson, 1883.

This drawing is a reduced version of the design for the hall at Bowood in the Soane Museum (S.M.D. Vol. 11, No. 79) where the flat area of the ceiling contains fifteen coffers rather than the nine shown here. This drawing matches the left-hand side of the larger ceiling exactly. When the main house at Bowood was demolished in 1955–6 this ceiling was moved to Lloyds offices in London. This ceiling is illustrated in Bolton 1922, Vol. I, Chapter 11.

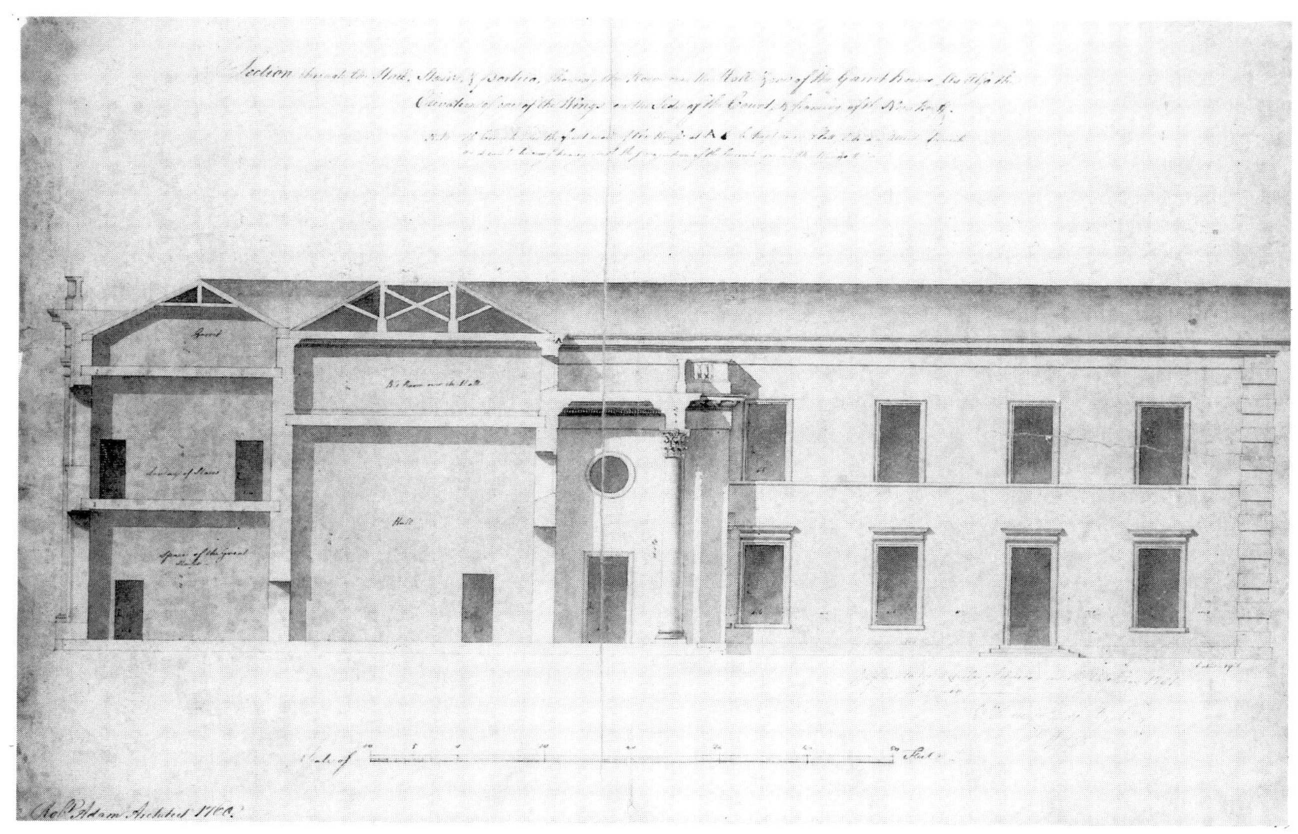

PLATE 21 (cat. 53)

COMPTON VERNEY, near Kineton, Warwickshire

Designs (on 2 sheets) for alterations to the entrance front and hall for Lord Willoughby de Broke. 1760.

53 Contract drawing; a sectional elevation of the entrance court, loggia, hall and staircase. The façade of the side of the court, a restrained four-bay, two storey design. Ashlar with delicately scaled architraves. The façade across the courtyard – shown in section – is lower and more elaborate with a colonnade of free-standing Corinthian columns, supporting a full entablature and balustrade. Giant order Doric columns appear in section on the garden front. (pl. 21).

Scale: 2 in. to 10 ft.

Signed bottom left *Robt Adam Architect 1760* and endorsed *Referred to by Articles of Agreement the 28 Febry 1761 Willoughby de Broke, Wm Hiorn*. Insc. In Adam's hand, *Section through the Hall, Stairs and Portico, showing the Room over the Hall and one of the Garret Rooms, as also the Elevation of one of the Wings on the side of the Court, framing of the New Rooff* [sic]. *N.B. The Cornish over the front Wall of the House at A, to be kept very flatt* [sic] *like an Attick* [sic] *Cornish as it would be very heavy with the projection of the Cornish round the wings etc.* Inscribed with dimensions and notes on uses of rooms, e.g. *Garret/Bed Room over the Hall/Landing of Stairs/Space of the Great Stairs/Hall.*

Pen and ink with grey wash and water-colour 472x725

E.1-1937

Prov.: Given by Dr W. L. Hildburgh, 1937.

54 Design for the entrance hall. Elevations of a great room, 27 ft. 10 in. by 57 ft. 6 in., with the sides 'folded down' and detached from the plan whose walls are also fully shown. A late Palladian scheme, dominated by a generous coved ceiling 25 ft. 4 ins. high and handsome, though not elaborate detail. The window wall is of five bays with tall round-headed sash windows, and a central door. It faces a central pedimented doorcase flanked by a pair of heavy and boldly scaled chimney pieces. One end of the room is screened by a Doric colonnade.

Insc. *Design for finishing the Hall at Compton* with indications of sizes.

Pen and ink and grey wash 509x694

E.2-1937

Prov.: Given by Dr W. L. Hildburgh, 1937.

Adam visited Compton Verney in September 1760: the alterations to the house set in hand the same year represent one of his earliest substantial commissions after his return from Italy. While the note about the visual effect of the cornice on the entrance elevation (and also the rather unorthodox entablature above the Corinthian columns which omits an architrave) both indicate the freedom to compose which was to become one of the hallmarks of the Adam style, the proposal for

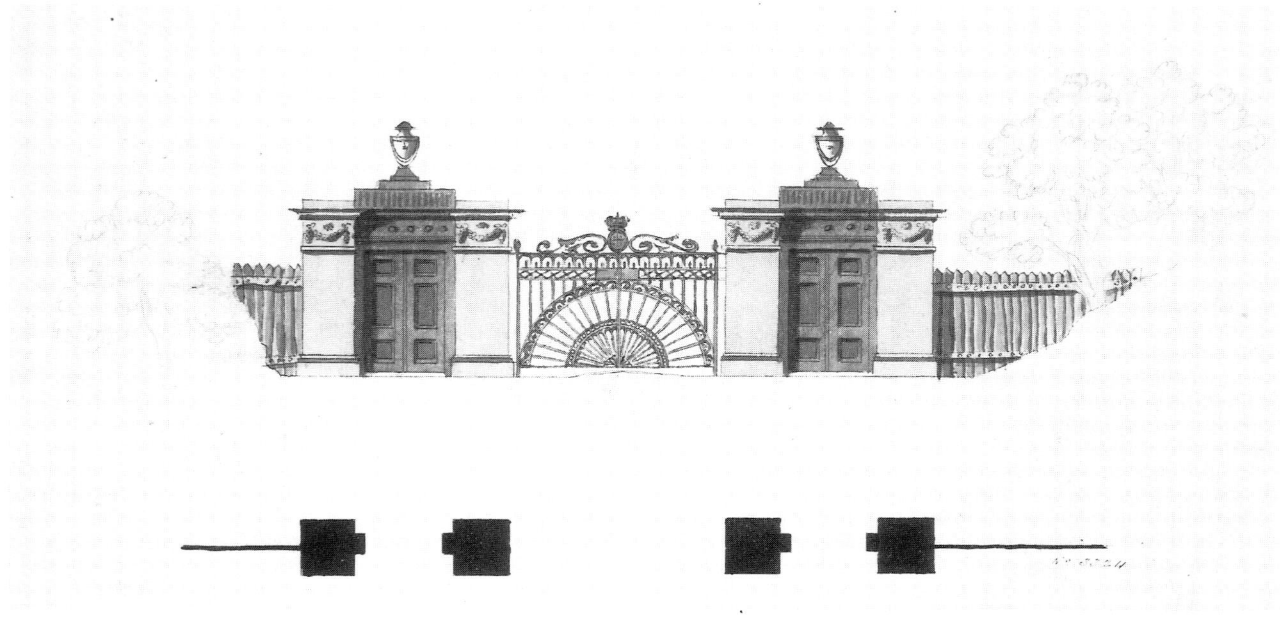

PLATE 22 (cat. 55)

the hall, like some of the work at Hatchlands and Shardeloes about this time, is comparatively conservative owing more to Burlington, Gibbs or Ware than to Robert's continental experience. It may be noted that in the hall the circular upper windows which appear in the contract drawing section have disappeared to accommodate the main cornice and coved ceiling. The proportion and dimensions of the hall matches nonetheless in both drawings and the corridor, above the Doric screen in the hall, lines in on the level of the landing of the great stairs. The house is discussed fully in Bolton 1922, vol. 1, pp. 216–228.

CROOME D'ABITOT, Worcestershire, Croome Court

Design for Park Gates for the Earl of Coventry, c.1781?

55 Sketch designs of the plan and elevation for a gateway within the park at Croome. A wrought-iron gate, 7 ft. by 11 ft. is flanked by paired ashlar piers each containing heavy six-panel timber doors which are surmounted by a blocking course and iron lamp. Timber paling extends the design to lightly sketched trees on either side. (pl. 22).

Scale: $2\frac{1}{8}$ in. to 10 ft.

Insc. in an office hand *Lord Coventry* and *Albemarle Street*, and *verso* in an uneducated hand *Earl of Coventry at Croome Put aside* and in pencil *£40 to 50*.

Pencil, ink and grey wash 298x480

3324

Prov.: C. J. Richardson.

The outline of this drawing, in pencil and ink inscribed 'Unknown', is in the Soane Museum (S.M.D. Vol. 51, No. 96). The design is intended to be seen from both sides. It makes no provision for a gate keeper – the doors are not lodges and lead nowhere – and being on a small scale, the gates are clearly intended to act as a visual punctuation within the park at Croome and may be related to the garden house for which designs were prepared in 1781 (*see* S.M.D. Vol. 51, No. 84). This design was not built.

CROOME D'ABITOT, Worcestershire, Church of St James the Apostle

Designs (on 2 sheets) for Gothic traceried windows with stained glass for the sixth Earl of Coventry. c.1760.

56 Sectional elevation of the chancel showing a 'Gothick' altar rail and three-light, mullioned East window, with intersecting Y tracery, daggers and cusps. Sunburst haloes in each light contain the dove of the Holy Spirit, the name of God and the monogram of Christ, with the sun and the moon with the symbol of the trinity above. Scale given.

Insc. *windows of the Church at Croome for the Right Hon*[ble], *The Earl of Coventry*.

Pen and ink, pencil with water-colour 440x315

3436.4

Prov.: C. J. Richardson.

57 Elevation of an elaborate stained glass window: six lights arranged in pairs with intermediate transom and a large rose window at the apex. Four apostles in the upper tier with a pair of angels in prayer and a pictorial scene of the last supper below.

Insc. *Croome Church design for stained glass for the Earl of Coventry*.

Pen and ink with water-colour 480x368

3436.5

Prov.: C. J. Richardson.

PLATE 23 (cat. 58)

Croome Church was built to designs by Adam between 1760 and 1763. The chancel as built accords with this drawing though plain quarries replace the stained glass shown here. The more elaborate design does not appear to have been used. The church is illustrated in Bolton 1922, Vol. I, p. 187.

GOSFORD HOUSE, East Lothian

Park gate for the seventh Earl of Wemyss. 1791.

58 Front elevation of a Doric gateway with lower screen walls each ending in a sphinx and containing round-headed pedestrian arches. Paired baseless Doric columns, flank the central carriage arch which is square headed – the entablature of the columns continuing across it – and is surmounted by a low attic storey with a shallow pediment, broken to admit a semi-circular sculpted panel of two lions facing a central urn. (pl. 23).

Insc. in an office hand *Extends 65 feet.*

Ink with grey washes 278 x 496

3326

Prov.: C. J. Richardson.

Adam's work for Lord Wemyss is documented in drawings at Gosford, in the correspondence of his chief clerk in Edinburgh, John Paterson, and in drawings in the Soane Museum. Designs for the house as built are dated 29 October, 1790 and were 'corrected' or up-dated a year later on 2 July 1791. Amongst the drawings at the house is one of a sphinx, similar to those shown here, though larger, with the note 'gave Mr Selby commission at Lord Wemyss' desire for two Spinxes [sic] 7 ft. by 4 ft.3 from this 23^d March 1790 £30 each spinx or £60 the pair'. Work at Gosford was thus a reality by the spring of 1790 and continued until 1800 after the death of Robert and James (see Hunt 1971, and McWilliam 1978, p. 222). Copies of Lord Wemyss's drawings are in the National Monuments Record for Scotland; other Adam proposals included a picturesque circular thatched cottage lodge, a low gateway with paired sphinx pedestals, dated 29 March 1791, and a larger squarely massed thatched lodge with pyramid roofs and rustic bark columns.

The austere character of this late gateway indicates clearly the new direction in which Robert's architecture was moving towards the end of his life. He has begun to use Greek Doric – Greek in its lack of any base and in the sharp arrises of its fluting if not in its still Roman capital – and the decorative elements which tend to be fewer are less pretty, more formal and on a larger scale. It is this late Adam manner which was to be taken over and to become very much the personal style of the Glasgow architect, David Hamilton in the early nineteenth century.

The Doric gateway was intended 'to be built on the entrance fence or Ha-Ha wall at Gosford'. It reached the stage of sized working drawings completed on 6 April 1791 in the Edinburgh office but was never carried out. Adam offered a choice of two slightly different designs of which this is the less elaborate. The selected design was larger, replacing the screen walls of this scheme with a pair of rooms for the gatekeeper and ending in coupled Doric columns to support the pedestals and sphinxes. Beyond these were further screen walls providing yards. The rear elevation was to have had coupled pilasters in place of the columns. Both versions of the design are recorded in an Adam sketches volume (S.M.D. Vol. 2, No. 151 and 152; see also Vol. 10, No. 95 and Vol. 51, No. 52).

HAREWOOD, North Yorkshire, Harewood House

Detailed designs (on 2 sheets) for Iron Handrails Front Iron railings, stone plinth and sphinx, for Edwin Lascelles.

59 Elevation of the design of an iron balustrade with lamp standards. The rail extends some 23 ft. and is set between the front of the building and a stone plinth which has ram's head terminals at each corner, and a stone sphinx above. The sphinx has been redrawn over an erased design.

Insc. with horizontal dimensions and on *verso For Edwin Lascelles Esq.*

Pen and ink and wash 204x527

3333

Prov.: C. J. Richardson.

Lit. & repr.: Bolton 1922, p. 174.

This elegant design would seem to be a proposal for the side railing of the paved platform and retaining walls before the main portico of the house. The base of one half column is accommodated at the right end of the design. The pattern of the railing a repeated anthemion motif contained within an inverted heart shape, or the spade of a pack of cards, is a characteristic Adam design occurring frequently as in the balconies of the Adelphi development in London. The design does not appear to have been used: the entrance front of Harewood, the result of collaboration between Robert Adam and John Carr of York, was altered by Sir Charles Barry from 1842 when the retaining walls were cut back and a stone balustrade built above them. Eighteenth-century views show Adam's plinth and sphinxes but not the railing in between. For a design for a chimney-piece, apparently for Harewood, see cat. 154.

60 Detailed design (or possibly working drawing) for a wrought-iron banister with mahogany hand rail. A complex pattern of interlaced diamond and heart shaped panels filled with open rosettes or vertical or inverted anthemion motifs. The hand rail carved with a Vitruvian scroll and beaded on the top. Pricked through.

Scale: $2\frac{3}{4}$ in. to 1 ft.

Insc. *Design of the Iron Rail & Hand Rail for the Principal Staircase of Gawthorp House* and *Section of the Mahogany Hand Rail* [sic] *at full Size.*

Ink and grey wash 340x442

3332

Prov.: C. J. Richardson.

Lit. & repr.: Bolton 1922, p.168.

This drawing has been folded into the shape normally associated with eighteenth-century bundles of documents and was presumably extracted by Richardson from a set of papers relating to building work at Harewood. Though the large scale of this drawing with the full-size profile of the handrail suggest that it was prepared for the use of tradesmen, the principal stair at Harewood is more simple in execution, though it uses the anthemion motifs that are a prominent feature here. Gawthorp House, mentioned in the inscription, is the old name for Harewood which was built by Edwin Lascelles from 1759 to replace Gawthorp Old Hall. Harewood House is well illustrated in Bolton 1922, Vol. I, chapter 9. For a detailed monograph on the house see Mauchline 1974.

KEDLESTON, Derbyshire, Kedleston Hall

Design for a Roman ruin.

61 Section and interior elevation of a high, brick-built, domed hall, 25 feet in diameter, with barrel vaulted side chambers elaborately decorated *all'antica*. Two figures examine the fragment of a cornice and a third is sketching in the domed area. (pl. 24).

Insc. by Richardson in pencil *Original Sketch by Robert Adam archt.*

Scale: $\frac{1}{2}$ in. to 1 ft.

Pen and ink on pencil with water-colour 610x960

3436.49

Prov.: C. J. Richardson.

Lit. & repr.: Harris 1987.

This drawing has twice been published as a design for the park at Kedleston: by Bolton (Bolton 1922, Vol. 1, p. 243) where it is dated 1761 and described as 'probably in connection with the bridge' and by Fleming (Fleming 1962, p. 266) where it is dated to 1758 and described as an 'ornamental ruin in a park, adapted for Kedleston'. Light pencil notes under the two side chambers (added by Richardson) repeat the inscriptions by Adam and Clérisseau on cat. 7 & 8 above, which are the original sketches, made in Rome, from which this design is developed. The central rotunda is reminiscent of domed halls in the baths at Hadrian's villa at Tivoli. The basis for Bolton's connecting the drawing with Kedleston is not now known and no reference is made to it in Leslie Harris's study of the drawings relating to the house and park at Kedleston.

LONDON, City, Drapers' Hall, Throgmorton Street

Design for a fanlight.

62 Detailed elevation, partly completed and coloured of a semi-circular fanlight to be worked in iron and brass. The radiating pattern of concentric semi-circles starts as a leaf rosette inside a guilloche band, there follows an extended anthemion motif contained within ten 'spokes', a second band of Vitruvian scroll show in brass colour and then a border of foliage arabesques and flower trumpets which extend the line of the spokes to a scalloped spider web pattern and the edge of the frame.

Insc. in an eighteenth-century hand, *This will come to about 13 Guineas* and *this to be Iron* and in a modern hand *Wrought iron and brass in Drapers Hall.*

Pen and ink, and grey and yellow water-colour. Silhouetted, width 355

Lent by the Drapers' Company.

The façade of the Drapers' Company hall was rebuilt in 1778 by John Gorham, 'an eminent surveyor and builder', who like the Adam brothers indulged in speculative developments in the city of London in the later 1770s and 1780s. The fanlight, executed according to this design and also on loan to the museum, is entirely characteristic of the brothers' style. Though no Adam drawings are known for the building, the existence of a ceiling design for the Drapers' Hall published by George Richardson, the brothers' chief clerk, in his *Book of Ceilings* suggests a connection between this work and the Adam office (see Colvin 1978, pp. 354 and 687).

PLATE 24 (cat. 61)

LONDON, City of Westminster, 38 Berkeley Square

Designs for a table and the frames of different mirrors 1770 (4 sheets) and for a chimneypiece (1 sheet) for the first floor drawing-rooms of Mr Robert Child's house.

63 Elevation of a console table and pier glass for the Front drawing-room. Gilt. Both severely rectangular. The table of four legs has a frame decorated with five half paterae of oval shape set inside detached hanging garlands. The looking glass has foliage arabesques and flower garlands at its base and a central vase and wave pattern at the top. 1770.

Scale: $8\frac{1}{4}$ in. to 6 ft.

Insc. in an office hand *Glass frame for front Drawing Room one pair stairs at Mr. Childs in Berkly Sq^r* and *35*.

Pen and sepia ink and water-colour 514x313

OPH 423–1949

Prov.: Osterley Park.

64 Elevation of a *Girandol* for the Front drawing-room. Gilt. A circular mirror, 3 ft. 6 in. in diameter, with four circular paterae attached at the top and bottom and at each side. Bell flower garlands hang from each of these with candle brackets of a late rococo character sprouting from the lower three. The mirror is framed by a reed and fillet moulding with a Vitruvian scroll fret applied to its outer edge. The flower garland at its base is circular while the top is extended as an arabesque finial on an open work lamp motif. 1770. (pl. 25).

Scale: $1\frac{3}{8}$in. to 1 ft.

Insc. in an office hand *Girandol opposite windows in front Drawing Room at Mr. Childs in Berkly Square* and *33*.

Pen and sepia ink with water-colour 530x445

OPH 426–1949

Prov.: Osterley Park.

65 Elevation of a pier glass for the Back Drawing-room. Gilt. Rectangular, 6 ft. 4 in. by 3 ft. 1 in. with square corners at the base and small quarter circles at the top. Foliage tendrils are applied at the base and a circular medallion of a female head in a beaded border is placed centrally at the top in an open roundel of foliage tendrils and bell garlands crowned by an acanthus finial. 1770.

Scale: $1\frac{1}{4}$ in. to 1 ft.

Insc. in an office hand with dimensions and *Glass for the Back Drawing Room at Mr. Child's in Berkly Square* and *34*. Dimensions indicated. Drawn scale of $1\frac{1}{4}$ in. to 1 ft.

Pen and sepia ink with water-colour 515x310

OPH 425–1949

Prov.: Osterley Park.

66 Elevation of a *Girandol* for the Back Drawing-room. Gilt. An oval glass, 2 ft. 11 in. by 2 ft. 5 in., is surmounted by an elaborate arabesque of foliage tendrils with a central cameo head, parasol and anthemion. It is supported on an equally elaborate, though heavier, arabesque base with winged griffons back to back immediately below the mirror itself, and four late rococo candle brackets at the base. 1770.

Scale: $1\frac{1}{4}$ in. by 1 ft.

Insc. in an office hand *Girandol opposite Chimney in Back Drawing Room at Mr Child's in Berkly Square.*

Pen and sepia ink with water-colour 515x310

OPH 424–1949

Prov.: Osterley Park.

Copies of these four handsome mirror designs (cat. 63–66) are S.M.D., Vol. 20, Nos. 38–41.

PLATE 25 (cat. 64)

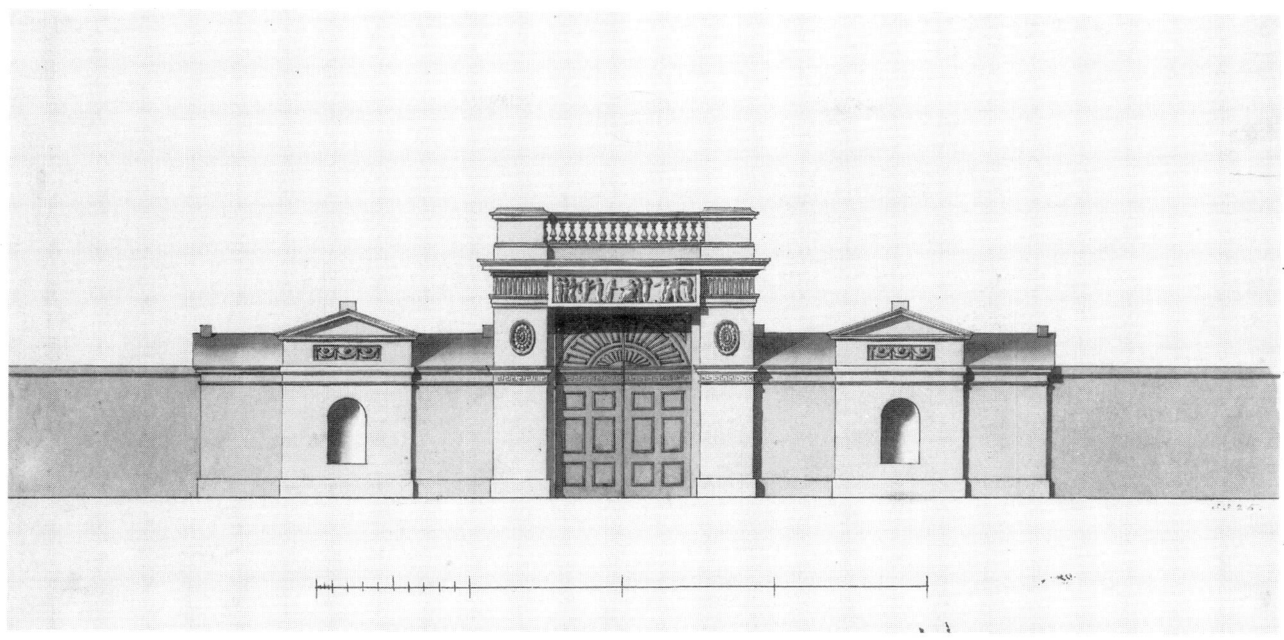

PLATE 26 (cat. 68)

67 Elevation of a chimneypiece. Conventional neo-classical design with Ionic half columns, anthemia on the frieze blocks, central plaque of a garlanded urn and greek key frieze between these. A second outline part elevation in pencil on the right shows the same design with a wider fireplace opening.

Insc. in pencil *3" 10 high/4" 0 wide/5" 4* and *4ft" 8in wide. This will be 2" wider than the Chimneypiece in the Back Drawing Room in Barkeley* [sic] *Sqr* and *38.*

Pen and red ink and pencil 180x390

OPH 428C–1949

Prov.: Osterley Park.

This chimney piece design, preserved with the Osterley papers, is not from the Adam office and must represent an independent proposal made for the Osterley family probably after Robert Child's death. The use of coloured wash and of a terracotta ink, the type of pale shadow that is cast, and the weak design all indicate a much more modest artist and origin. The proposed location for the chimney piece is not known.

LONDON, City of Westminster, Deputy Ranger's Lodge Gateway, Green Park

68 Front elevation: a tall gateway surmounted by a balustrade and flanked by low ashlar wings. The centre of each wing is marked by a slight projection, crowned by a pediment and decorated with a blank niche. (pl. 26).

Scale: $2\frac{1}{4}$ in. to 10 ft.

Pen and sepia ink with grey wash 265x480

3325

Prov.: C. J. Richardson.

Adam designed the Deputy Ranger's Lodge in the Green Park for Col. the Hon. Archibald Montgomerie, later the 11th Earl of Eglinton, in 1766. Plans and a perspectival view appear in Adam 1773 (Vol. III, Pls. xvi and xvii) dated 1768. This design for a gateway was prepared for Lord Eglinton's successor, Lord William Gordon (1744– 1823), brother of the 4th Duke of Gordon, who was appointed to the post of Deputy Ranger on the 13 February 1778. Lord William also intended to make alterations to the house. It is doubtful whether the gateway or any of this extra work was carried out. The Lodge was demolished in 1845.

Related designs in the Soane Museum drawings are three elevations in Vol. 51, Nos. 60 and 61. This drawing, probably made by a clerk in the Adam office, is a development from No. 61 which shows the balustrade as a pencilled addition, a different figure panel over the archway and lighter garlands beneath the pediments of the wings. The end sections of the balustrade over the arch were to have served as chimney pots.

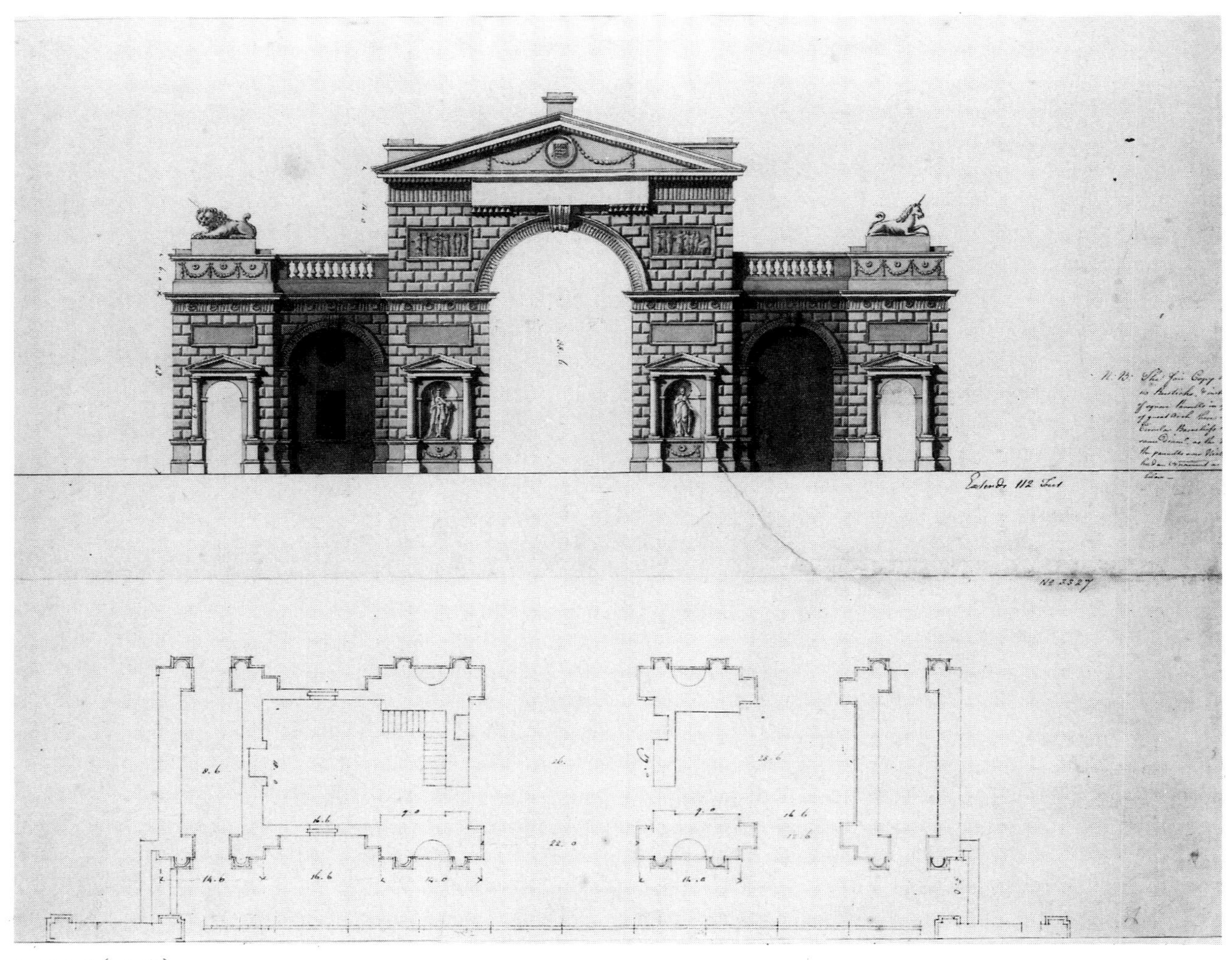

PLATE 27 (cat. 69)

LONDON, City of Westminster, Triumphal Gateway, Hyde Park Corner

69 Plan (in ink outline) and elevation (fully rendered) of an archway, weighbridge and toll house intended to close the road at the west end of Piccadilly. An heroic design 112 ft. wide with a pedimented central archway, 58 ft. in height, is flanked by tall wings that terminate in large scale sculptures of a lion and unicorn above pedestrian arches. These arches are contained within pedimented Doric aedicules that are repeated on the pier walls that support the central road arch and here contain statues of a king and queen set in arched niches. The whole façade is vigorously rusticated throughout. Pricked for transfer. c.1775. (pl. 27).

Insc. with various dimensions and in Adam's hand *Extends 112 Feet* and *N.B.: The fair Copy had no Rusticks and instead of square pannells in spand[rels] of Great Arch there were circular Basreliefs the same diamr. as the nich. The pannells over the niches etc. had an ornament as sketched below.* The elevation insc. faintly on *Verso No 17 Hyde Park Gateway*, *Put aside* [crossed out], *office copy* and with an old inscription relating the design to the offices at Syon.

Pen and ink with grey washes. Two sheets joined; the elevation 274 x 566 trimmed at the bottom and on the left; the plan 184 x 566

3327

Prov.: C. J. Richardson.

In 1778 Adam made designs for a lodge and gates at Hyde Park Corner (S.M.D. Vol. 51, Nos. 77–82). The scheme recorded here which is infinitely more ambitious and which bears the fateful inscription 'put aside' presumably pre-dates the 1778 project. When these grandiose proposals were drawn up is not known. Drawings in the Soane Museum record three different schemes for the gateway each of which envisages a deep courtyard on the east, or town side, of the archway with colonnaded or arcaded screens flanking side gates leading to Hyde Park and Constitution Hill (S.M.D. Vol. 28, Nos. 4–9). Of these designs the largest accords with the silhouette of the present elevation though the architecture is of the Corinthian Order with coupled columns rising the full height of the main arch block. This Doric scheme is evidently a variant of the largest design. Part of the layout plan in the Soane Museum (pl. 28) matches this plan exactly and established that Adam intended to place a weigh house in the northern archway and accommodation for the toll gatekeeper in the arch to the south, with pedestrian passage ways at either end. A curiosity of this elaborately architectural façade is that it would have been wider than the colonnaded blocks that framed the approach to it which overlap the outermost bays of the design by four feet. The layout plan which records the irregular huddle of small properties near St George's Hospital, which Adam's scheme would have replaced, does not suggest that any constraints inherent in the site dictated this overlapping of the

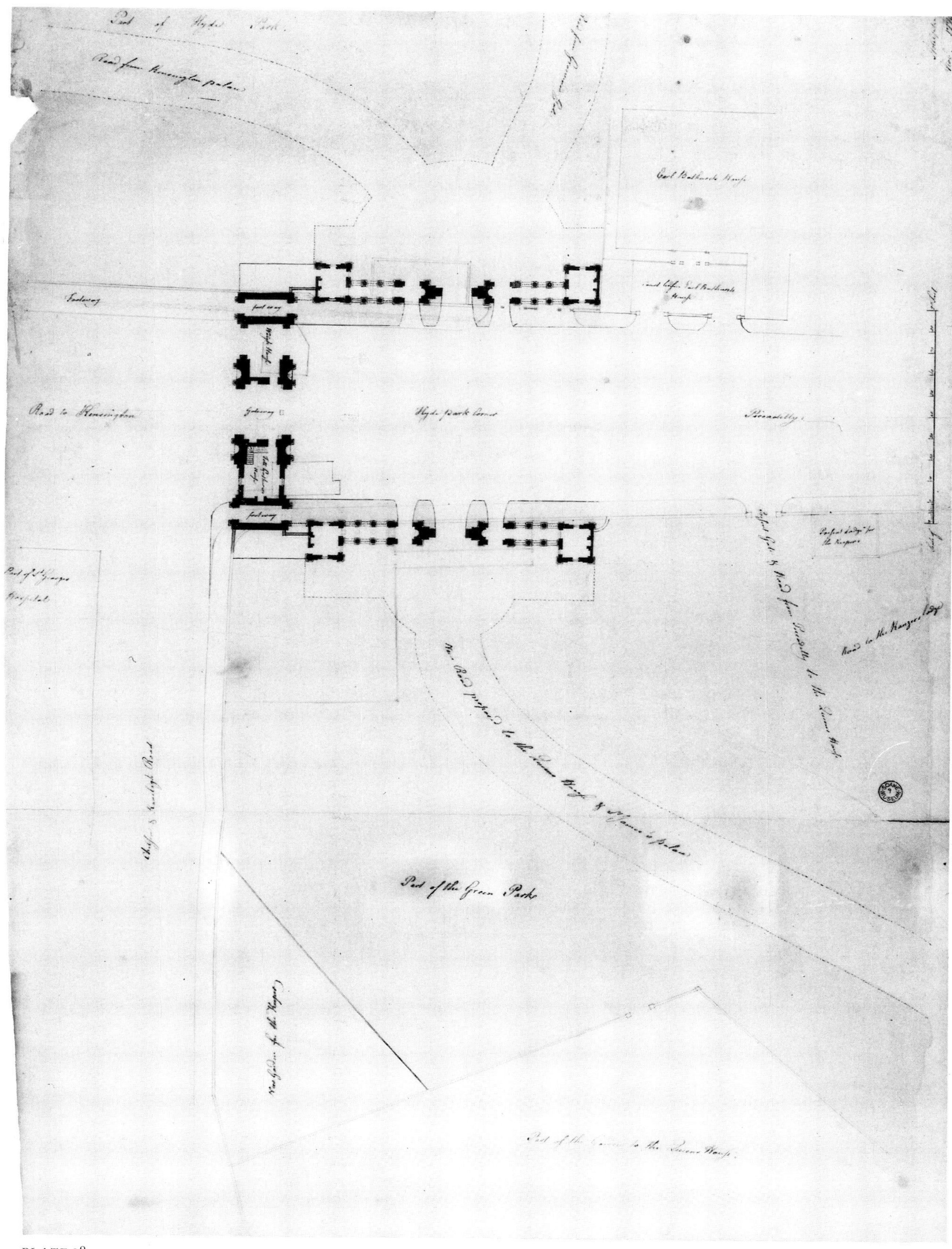

PLATE 28

different parts. On the contrary this must have been a conscious decision of the architect's to enhance the sense of movement and picturesque effect within the composition. It seems possible that Lord Apsley, Lord Chancellor from January 1771 to June 1778, and for whom Adam was working at Apsley House immediately adjacent to the Hyde Park corner site, may have been instrumental in securing this public commission. Apsley succeeded his father as 2nd Earl Bathurst in September 1775 and, as his property is marked on the layout plan as Lord Bathurst's, the Gateway scheme must be dated to that year or later.

This heroic proposal for Hyde Park Corner demonstrates Adam's ability in formal architecture at its very best. A design of grandeur and authority, it is marked with much of the distinctive personality of the architect, as apparent in the strictly organised proportional scheme of the entire façade as in its free and imaginative use of detail. In this triumphal entrance Adam builds up a system of inter-related arch openings and entablatures as dense and uncompromising as that of any sixteenth-century Italian architect: thus the pedestrian entry arches at either end of the screen are related to the relieving arches that flank the central block by the scale of the entablature of the aedicule which contains them. This entablature becomes, in the next bay of the design, the impost from which the relieving arch springs and this arch is itself contained within an area that is defined and limited by a second entablature tied by a keystone to the top of the arch. In the central block of the composition this second entablature (defined by the height of the arch beneath it) becomes the impost of the triumphal arch itself which rises to a third and final entablature to which it too is linked by a scrolled keystone. Thus the whole design builds up logically from the scale of the outermost pedestrian arches to the climax of the central opening and this climax is sustained in the increasing width of the units of the façade, read from the outer edges towards the centre as 15 ft., 17 ft., 15 ft. and 22 ft., or, if the whole centre block is taken as one unit, as 15 ft., 17ft. and 42 ft. In terms of formal analysis by bays the façade can thus be described as a rhythmic progression of a-b-c-b-a (when the central section is considered as a distinctive whole) or as a-b-a1-d-a1-b-a where the central section is broken down into its constitutent elements of piers with aedicule niches that balance the outermost pedestrian arches (a1) and the great central arch itself (d). Proportional relationships evident in this design are (i) the square used in the central block (c) with the centre of the arc of the arch placed fractionally above the intersection of its diagonals – a deviation from absolute geometry which Adam will have adopted as a visual adjustment occasioned by the entra height of the apex of the pediment – and (ii) the occurrence of golden-section rectangles in the central arch piers (a1) and the outermost bays (a) where the proportion of the height (taken as the base to the underside of the cornice) to the width is that of 1.618 to 1 or Ø (phi). The occurrence of this proportional relationship has been analysed by Professor David Fensom (1984) as an essential ingredient in the development of Adam elevational schemes. Golden section or Ø rectangles in British eighteenth-century architecture are also discussed by Robertson (1948). Details which are characteristic of Adam's approach to design are the non-antique fluted entablature of the pediment interrupted, in true Neo-classical taste, by the slab-like, blank central tablet; the massively scaled *guttae* (almost a foot in diameter) beneath the tablet and hinting at the doric order; and the frieze of the arch impost and screen wall entablature which is a common Adam invention alternating three vertical flutes and a patera as an unorthodox variation of a triglyph frieze. Finally the delicate counter point of Adam's use of garlands between the base of the statue niches and the pedestals beneath the lion and the unicorn should be noted as perhaps an unconscious memory of Michelangelo's Medici chapel tombs.

LONDON, City of Westminster (formerly St Marylebone), 13 Mansfield Street

Designs (on 2 sheets) for the ceilings of the front and back drawing rooms of a house built by John Devall. 1772.

70 Design for the front drawing room ceiling. Rectangular with spaces for three circular paintings in a line down the ceiling arranged about a large plasterwork design of circular bands radiating from the largest panel. The border is a frieze-like band of alternating urns and lily trumpets. It ends in a square panel at each corner with quarter wheel patterns extending from the border into the main field of the ceiling.

Pen and ink and grey wash 206x319

19541.4

Prov.: E. Parsons, 1864.

71 Design for the back drawing room ceiling. Rectangular, divided into three parts with a circular design filling the full width of the ceiling and half circle repeats added at either end. The centre is a plasterwork plaque in a plain frame surrounded by loops of flowerbell garlands attached by ribbon bows with straight drops hanging between the loops. The outer frame is a thin border of Vitruvian scroll with a larger flower-bell circle beyond it which touches the border of the ceiling. Six semi-circular patterns of griffons facing each other with a vase between them fill the spaces between the Vitruvian scroll circle and the central medallion which is filled with the figure of a female jug-bearer. The entire ceiling is contained in a guilloche border. (pl. 29).

Pen and ink and grey wash 172x335

19541.5

Prov.: E. Parsons, 1864.

Both these drawings appear to be early versions, prepared by an office draughtsman of limited skill, from preliminary sketches by Adam. They are matched by drawings in the Soane Museum (S.M.D. Vol. 13, Nos. 62 and 63) which, in each case, have been taken further as designs, accommodating for example the chimney breasts in the rooms which are not considered here, and generally tightening up and improving upon the details of individual motifs. The decorative band of the front drawing room ceiling has guilloche borders, is given more depth and its urns, which are taller and more substantial, face into rather than out of the room. The finished design for the back drawing room makes minor but significant additions to the foliage arabesques between the main parts of the ceiling and reduces the ends from a half-circle to a segmental pattern. It is fully coloured and proposes painted panels in place of medallions.

Mansfield Street was a speculative development undertaken by William Adam and Co., a real estate company established by the four Adam brothers in 1764. The street was developed from about 1770 with the Adams acting in association with different tradesmen. Devall who was a builder appears to have been one of these. The ceiling designs in the Soane Museum are dated 1772: by 1774 the house was complete and inhabited by Lord Dillon while John Devall had moved on to build a

PLATE 29 (cat. 71)

PLATE 30 (cat. 72)

house as part of another Adam scheme at Portland Place, for which the brothers designed chimneypieces, ceilings and friezes in 1775 and 1776 (see Spiers, pp. 42, 46 and 68); the minute of an estimate and agreement by the Adam brothers to build another house in Mansfield Street in December 1771 for the Dowager Countess of Warwick, for £8,241, is in the British Library (Add M.S. 40714 ff 110–114).

No. 13 Mansfield Street still exists and was to be lived in by two celebrated English architects: J. L. Pearson from 1881 to 1897 and Sir Edwin Lutyens from 1919 to 1944. The ceilings recorded in these drawings also survive though the painted panels in the roundels, if Mr Devall ever installed them, have been replaced by nineteenth-century rosettes of acanthus leaf and round leaf bosses, and extra flat bands similar to the guilloche borders though plain have been added (by Lutyens?) beyond the outer edges of each design.

LONDON, City of Westminster, Piccadilly House, Piccadilly

Design for a screen wall for Lord Holland.

72 Outline elevation of a long single storey screen. A Doric pediment is flanked by solid screen walls that terminate in slightly advanced end bays with low pyramid roofs. The carriage arch is framed by Adamesque pilasters supporting a decorated impost which continues as a cornice across the entire front. In the end bays the arch motif is repeated with a Diocletian window inside the arch and a plain window below. The links between the end bays and the central arch have low flat-headed doorways flanked by urns in niches with a long plaque of oakleaf garlands and paterae filling the attic above. (pl. 30).

Insc. on the *verso Adam's designs for Melbourne House*.

Pen and ink 378x603

3835

Prov.: C. J. Richardson.

A finished wash drawing of this design, for the site of the present Albany, is in the Soane Museum (S.M.D. Vol. 51, No. 68) inscribed *Design of a Porte Cochere for the House of the Right Honble Lord Holland in Piccadilly* and is noted on the side at the back (for reference when rolled up) *Lord Holland's Gateway, Number 12*. No other drawings from this set have been preserved. This drawing differs from the finished design only in the windows of the end bays which are replaced by doors to match the central archway. Lord Holland sold Piccadilly House to Lord Melbourne in 1770 and Adam subsequently made plans for a different house on the site (see Index p. 45). This design with its meretricious accumulation of small details over the whole façade may be compared with the finish of the Adelphi elevations and was evidently intended to be executed in stucco. A sketch design, noted *Ionick of Le Roi* (S.M.D. Vol. 9, No. 195), suggests that Adam at one stage intended to take the order from J. D. Le Roy's *Plus Beaux Monuments de la Grece*, though in the finished design it is one of his own discoveries, the Lotus type capital from Diocletian's Palace at Split, that is pressed into service with an unusually orthodox Doric frieze.

LONDON, City of Westminster, 106 (formerly 29) Piccadilly

Design for the decoration of a bed recess for the Earl of Coventry.

73 Elevation and part plan of a screen of four columns across the end of a room. The recess is 11 ft. high and 12 ft. wide in a wall 16 ft. long with a plain Ionic room cornice. The proposed screen has natural palm tree column shafts with fronds sprouting from near the top to reveal an invented capital of acanthus leaves with a large pineapple in the centre. The columns form an a-b-a rhythm of narrow and wide spacings and are quarter engaged at the corners of the bed recess.

Insc. in pencil with dimensions and *Design for an Alcove for the Rt Hon the Earl of Coventry's Bedchamber in room/R. Adam.*

Pen and ink and wash 295x333

3436.14

Prov.: C. J. Richardson.

In a letter to Lord Kames of 1763 Adam put forward the idea that the origin of the Corinthian capital, despite the pretty story told by Vitruvius and all subsequent commentators down to his own day, was more likely to have been derived from primitive building techniques when roughly cleaned tree trunks were used as columns with their smaller branches and leaves still left partly complete at the tops. The notion, while equally as improbable as the Vitruvian tale, may here be relevant as it goes some way to explain the fantasy of this essentially decorative scheme for a palm tree column screen to Lord Coventry's bed. Though this design was not carried out Adam did make use of a similar device in designs for a tea pavilion at Moor Park, built for Sir Laurence Dundas about 1765 (S.M.D., Vol. 32, Nos. 44–46 and Vol. 46, Nos. 168–169 *see* also Bolton 1922, Chapter 2) and in a scheme for an unidentified interior with naturally coloured slender trunks and palm branches in place of columns (S.M.D., Vol. 50, No. 93). John Webb in 1663 had made an essentially similar design to cat. 73 for an alcove in the King's bedchamber at Greenwich Palace which, though it was not to be executed was published in John Vardy *Some Designs of Inigo Jones* in 1744 and will thus have been known to Adam. It was also used by John Vardy as the basis for Lord Spencer's room at Spencer House in 1757 (Friedman 1987, pl. II and 20). In Webb's design Corinthian capitals still appear above the palm fronds however (see Harris 1971, p. 24 and Fig. 129).

LONDON, Barnet. (formerly Middlesex), Hendon Manor

Design for a bridge for David Garrick.

74 Elevation of a bridge with two segmental arches and large floral paterae in the spandrels. To be built of worn masonry with the cornices and coping stones artificially weathered and the parapets extended beyond the river by criss-cross timber railings. The central iron lampstand is incongrously spruce. Pricked through ruled border. (pl. 31).

Insc. in pencil by William Adam (?) *Bridge over the Esk at Dalkeith* and on *verso* by A. T. Bolton *possibly for David Garrick, Hendon Manor.*

Pencil, pen and ink and grey wash 290x446

3334

Prov.: C. J. Richardson.

A finished version of this drawing with a section through the bridge and a plan of the piers is in the Soane Museum (S.M.D. Vol. 51, No. 26) inscribed 'For Mr. Garrick at Hendon'. David Garrick lived at No. 5 Adelphi Terrace, or at his villa at Hampton: he also owned a manor at Hendon the sale of which was under discussion in 1767 (*see* Bolton 1922, Vol. II, notes to Spier's Index p. 16). This design relates to that property, now known as Hendon Hall or Hendon Place. The convention of a partially ruined though usable structure, which Adam proposes here, is typical of the Picturesque approach of many later eighteenth-century architects to garden building design. At about the same time that this design was made the architect had prepared an elaborate scheme for a five arched ruined bridge 'in imitation of the Aqueducts of the Ancients, proposed to be built over the lake at Bowood Park in Wiltshire'.

PLATE 31 (cat. 74)

The design for Bowood is illustrated as Plate 7 in the second volume of Adam 1773. Like Garrick's bridge at Hendon it was not to be built though Adam finally did succeed in building a semi-ruined viaduct and bridge in 1780 as an evocative element in the approach to Culzean Castle in Ayrshire.

The picturesque effect of a semi-ruined bridge evidently appealed to Robert Adam and will have been familiar to him, not only from his Roman experience but also from the fashion in English rococo gardens of closing a vista with a hoarding on which a Roman ruin might be depicted. Batty Langley publishes designs for such ruin pieces in *New principles of Gardening*, 1728 and a ruined bridge scene appeared at Vauxhall gardens in 1751 and on other occasions. (*See* V. & A. 1984, F. 17).

LONDON, Hounslow, (formerly Middlesex), Church of St Leonard, Heston

Design for the monument to Robert Child, 1782.

75 Elevation of a large wall monument with two putti bearing an inverted torch, the symbol of death, and a circle, the symbol of eternity, beside a funerary urn. This sculptural group is set above a flat sarcophagus flanked by plinths which support candelabrae. A broad truncated pyramid, rising behind the putti and urn, supports a smoking vase.

Insc. on the sarcophagus *This Monument was erected in Memory of Robert Child of Osterley Park Esqr who died the 28 of July 1782 Aged 43. He married Sarah Daughter of Gilbert Fodrell Esqr by whom he left one Daughter Sarah Countess of Westmorland.*

Pen and ink and wash 214x93

E. 973–1965

Prov.: Bequeathed by Rupert Gunnis, J.P.

While this monument, carved by the sculptor, Peter Matthias Van Gelder (1739–1809), is comparable with other funerary designs by Robert Adam, this drawing appears to be a copy made for or by the sculptor and is not from the Adam office. The existing monument bears the names of Adam and Van Gelder.

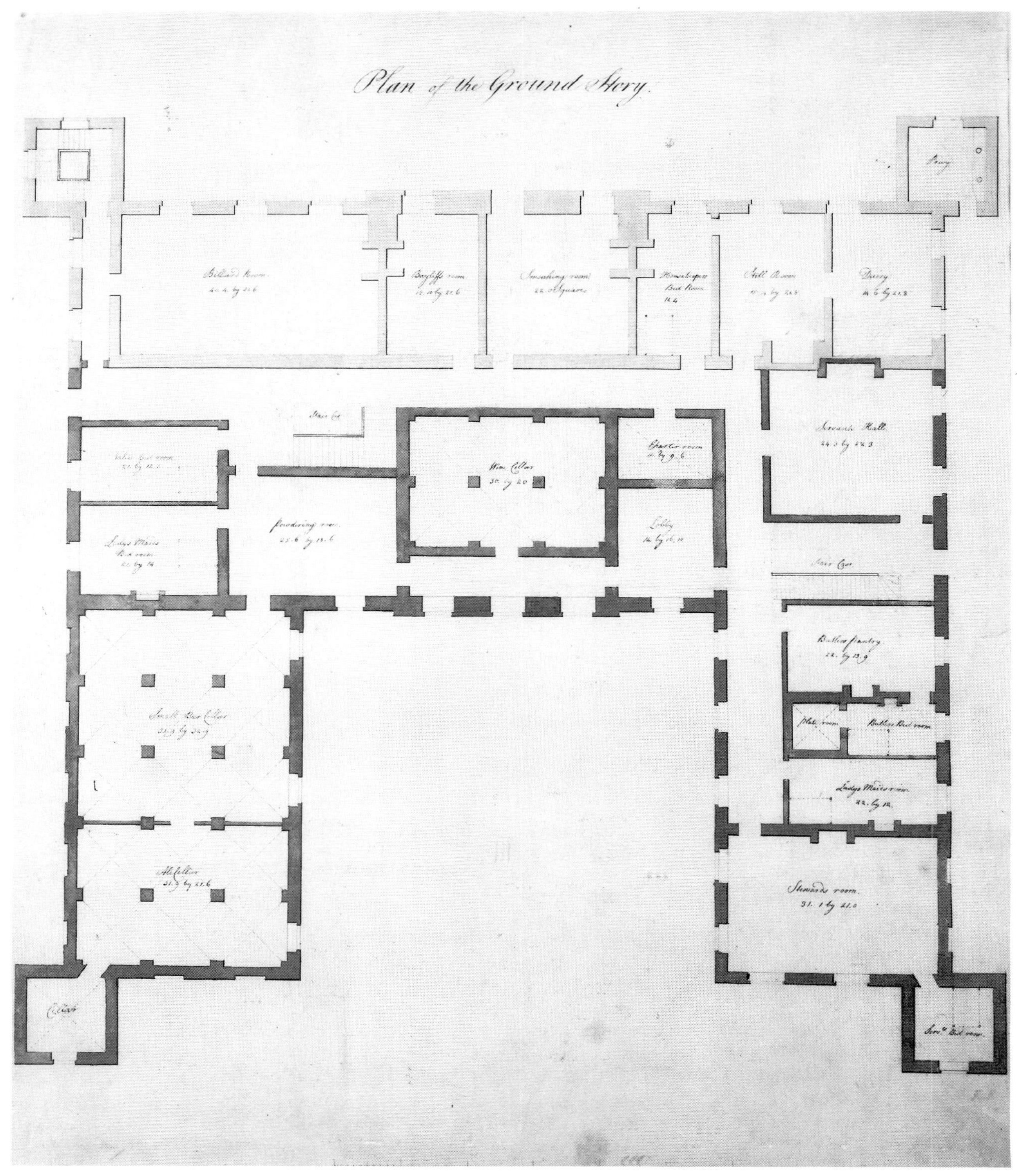

PLATE 32 (cat. 76)

LONDON, Hounslow, (formerly Middlesex), Osterley Park

Designs (on 5 sheets) for alterations and additions in a Palladian style for Francis Child, 1761.

76 Ground floor Plan. Proposed additions in black and the existing west front and terminal towers shown in red. The plan shows only servants' accommodation and cellarage with the exception of the *Billiard Room*, *Bayliffs room* and the *Smoaking* room on the west front. (pl. 32).

Scale: $1\frac{1}{8}$ in. to 10 ft.

Insc. in office copperplate *Plan of the Ground Story* and with names and dimensions of rooms. s. bottom left *Robt Adam Architect 1761.*

Pen and ink and wash with water-colour 530x440

OPH 428E–1949

Prov.: Osterley Park.

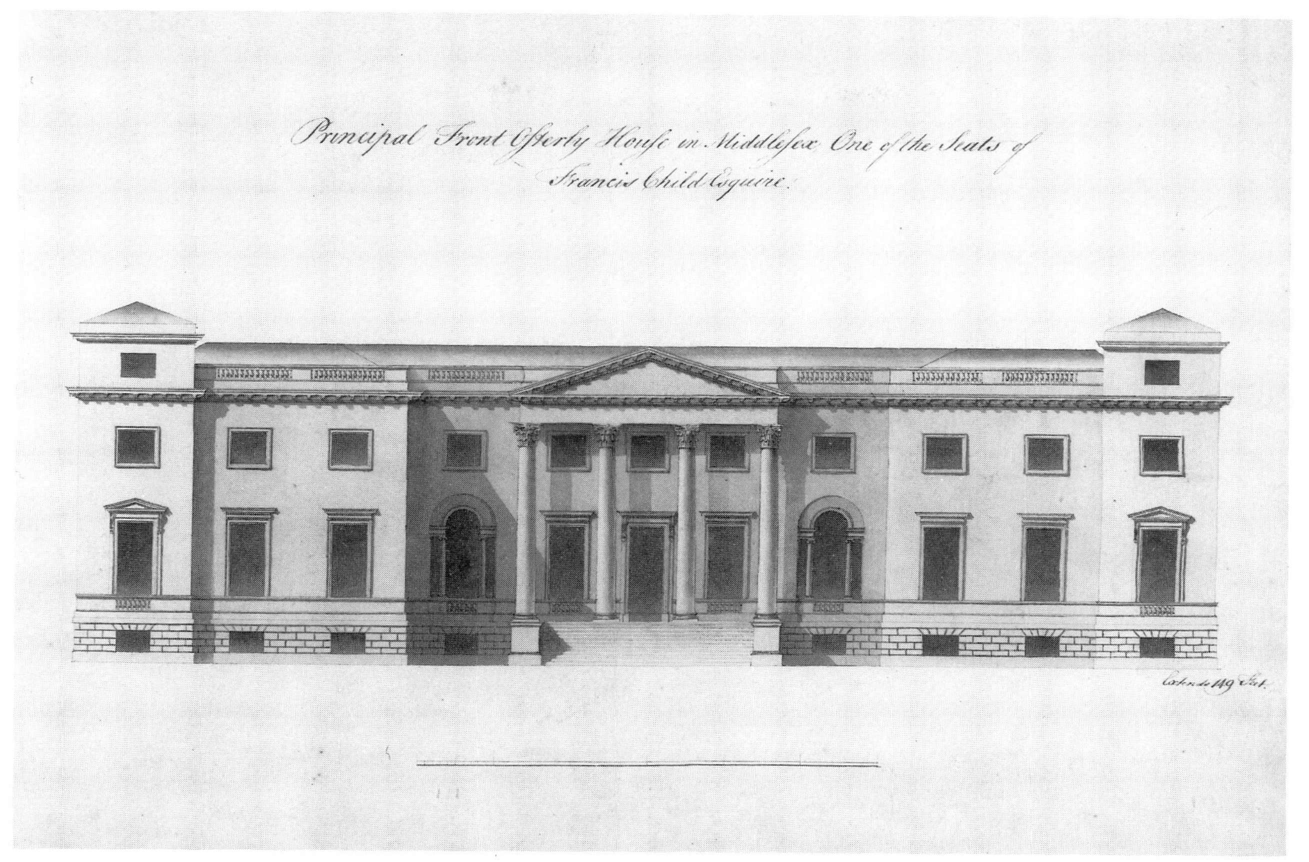

PLATE 33 (cat. 77)

77 East or entrance elevation of the Palladian scheme. Two storeys on a rusticated semi-basement with ashlar above and a balustraded roof line. A U-shaped façade with deeply recessed five-bay centre, flanked by two-bay wings with single-bay towers projecting from the extreme corner of each wing. The towers, raised by a shallow attic above the cornice level of the rest of the house, have pyramid roofs. In the centre, a free-standing tetra-style Corinthian portico, on a temple front flight of steps, flanked by Venetian windows in relieving arches. (pl. 33).

Scale: $1\frac{1}{8}$ in. to 10 ft.

Insc. in office copperplate *Principal Front of Osterly House in Middlesex One of the Seats of Francis Child Esquire / Extends 149 Feet*. S. bottom left *Robt Adam Architect 1761*.

Pen and ink and wash 330 x 510

OPH 411–1949

Prov.: Osterley Park.

A copy of this drawing exists in the Soane Museum (S.M.D. Vol. 43, No. 92). It is essentially the same excepting some minor alterations to the architraves of the windows on the main floor and the addition of pediments over those of the two end bays of each wing.

78 Elevation of the South front of the Palladian scheme. A long twelve-bay three-storey façade, rusticated on the ground floor. The end bays treated as terminal towers rising by a shallow attic above the cornice level of the house. The West tower – pre-existing – has heavy quoins and a string course that breaks the line of the main roof cornice.

Scale: $1\frac{1}{8}$ in. to 10 ft.

Insc. in office copperplate *South Front of Osterly House*. S. at bottom left *Robt Adam Architect 1761*.

Pen and ink and wash 335 x 510

OPH 414–1949

Prov.: Osterley Park.

79 Elevation of the North front of the Palladian scheme. Essentially the same as cat. 78 above.

Scale: $1\frac{1}{8}$ in. to 10 ft.

Insc. in a less skilful office hand *North Front of Osterly House*. S. at bottom left *Robt Adam Architect 1761*.

Pen and ink and wash 427 x 600

OPH 410–1949

Prov.: Osterley Park.

An outline copy of this drawing exists in the Soane Museum (S.M.D., Vol. 43, No. 93).

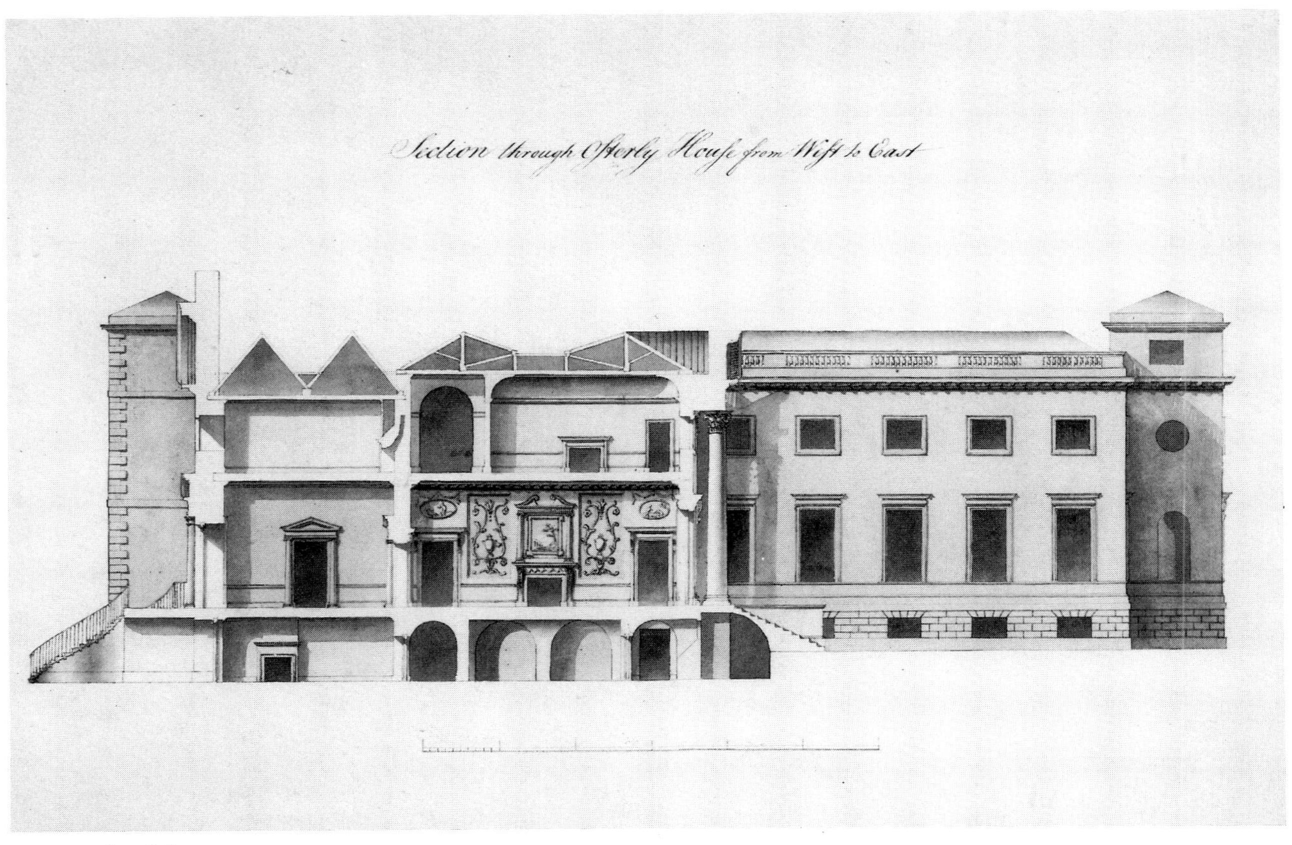

PLATE 34 (cat. 80)

80 Sectional elevation through the entrance hall and saloon, with the south façade of the court of the Palladian scheme. (pl. 34).

Scale: $1\frac{1}{8}$ in. to 10 ft.

Insc. in office copperplate *Section through Osterly House from West to East.* s. at bottom left *Robt Adam Architect 1761.*

Ink and wash 330x510

OPH 413–1949

Prov.: Osterley Park.

An outline copy of this drawing exists in the Soane Museum (S.M.D. Vol. 43, No. 95).

Adam had two clients at Osterley the brothers Francis and Robert Child, sons of Samuel Child, the senior partner of Child's bank. Francis Child came of age in 1756. It was he who commissioned the first set of designs of 1761 to regularise and largely replace the late Elizabethan house built by Sir Thomas Gresham between 1570 and 1577, which had been purchased by his uncle, Sir Francis Child sometime Lord Mayor of London in 1726. Of the old house little remains in the main building. Bolton considered that sections of the roof had been retained from the first structure (Bolton 1922, Vol. 1, p. 302) though this seems unlikely as both Sir William Chambers and another anonymous designer – perhaps Sir Robert Taylor? – whose plan for alterations is preserved at the house had been consulted by Francis Child and the west front of the house had been recast from 1756 well before Adam made his first proposals. It is this front that appears as a nine bay range, one room thick, with square towers at either end on Adam's plan cat. 76 above. For a discussion of Chambers's connection with Osterley see Harris 1970, p. 240.

Francis Child killed himself in the summer of 1763 when Osterley descended to his brother Robert who then became head of the banking firm of Francis Child and Co. Under Robert Child the house was to be enlarged by extending the wings of the entrance court for a further 20 ft., by the addition of the double portico between them (see cat. 81), by an elaborately shaped new entrance hall and by greatly enriched interior decorations. The drawings which follow are all for this work for Robert Child. Osterley is described in Bolton 1922, Vol. 1, Chap. 15.

81 Elevation of the entrance front of the house as built. A hexastyle Ionic portico, set on a broad temple-front flight of steps (also shown in plan), and flanked by two three-bay, three-storey ranges with tall single-bay corner towers rising a full storey above the parapet of the rest of the house. Acroterion statues on the pediment and ogee roofs to the towers with large pinecone finials. Quoins on the tower corners to match those on the earlier towers of the west front. All the windows without architraves. Sketch of an iron lampstandard. There are alterations in pencil. (pl. 35).

Scale: $1\frac{1}{4}$ in. to 10 ft.

Insc. in office copperplate *East Front of Osterly House in Middlesex. The Seat of Robert Child Esqr.*

Pen and ink and grey wash with pencil 450x620

OPH 412–1949

Prov.: Osterley Park.

An interesting side-light on Adam's methods of dealing with his clients is suggested by this drawing. It presents his revolutionary proposal to close the U-shaped entrance

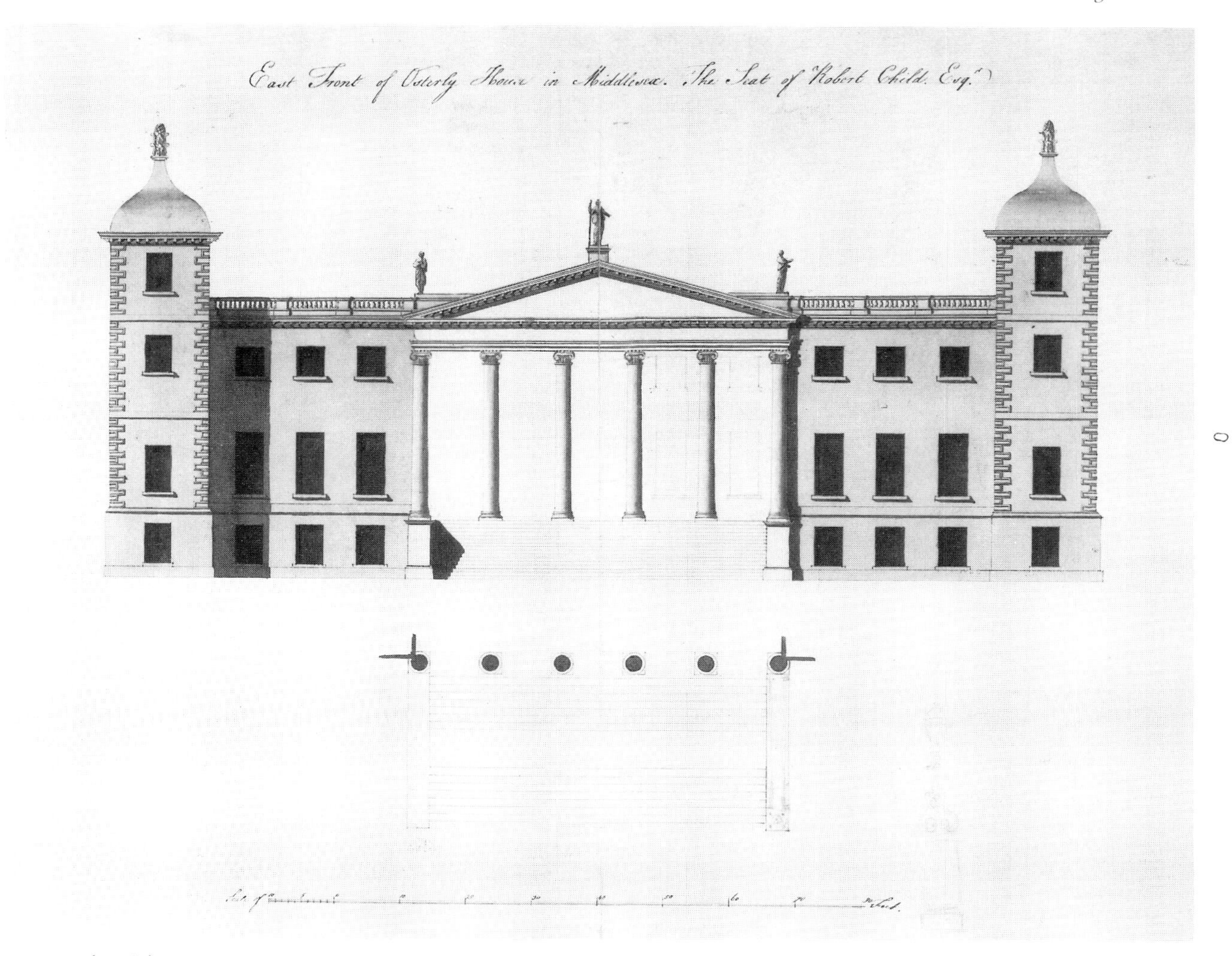

PLATE 35 (cat. 81)

PLATE 36 Osterley Park from the north east. (National Monuments Record.)

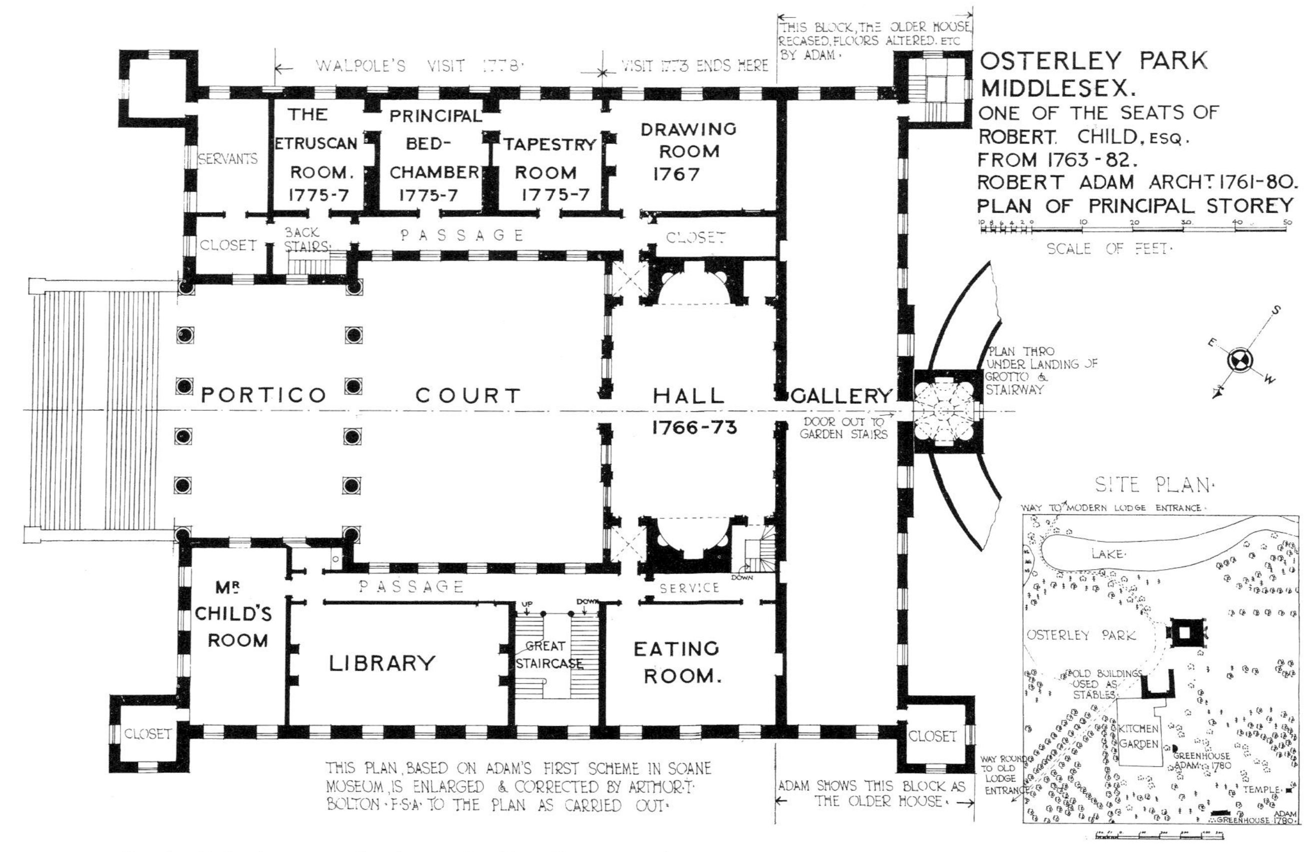

PLATE 37 Osterley Park, plan as completed 1763–82. (From Bolton 1922.)

courtyard, suggested in earlier schemes for Francis Child (see Cat. 76–80 above) by a screen of columns, yet by comparison with those schemes it is much less carefully drawn. The elevation is almost slapdash with washes which are crudely applied, and which jump awkwardly from pale grey to intense black. Lacking in subtlety, they give the house a bleak air that is not enhanced by the decision to omit the door and windows of the entrance elevation at the end of the courtyard. The drawing bears an office title and scale but omits any indication of the length of the front and is neither signed nor dated. On the other hand it is amongst the framed clients drawings preserved at the house and must therefore have been shown by Adam to Child to explain his ideas. The pencil additions are exactly that, *explanations* for a client: hence the soft pencil doodle of a lamp bracket at the end of the plinth of the retaining wall for the stairs and the lightly sketched indication of the windows within the first two intercolumations of the right side of the portico. Robert Child we may imagine (or perhaps infer) could not read the drawing which Adam had brought to show off his most recent, and most original, idea. But the architect himself was at hand to explain its novelties and, no doubt, the scope for *movement* that the scheme contained.

82 Sized elevation of the front and side of the pedestal of the retaining wall beside the entrance steps. Plain ashlar with moulded base and cornice; sphinx above.

Scale: 7 in. to 10 ft.

Insc. in an office hand *Pedestal at the foot of the Portico at Osterly.* sizes given *6/9.2/3.4/4.5.*

Pen and ink and wash 325 x 460

OPH 422–1949

Prov.: Osterley Park.

This design was not used in the steps as built which have eagle terminals and no sphinx.

83 Outline elevation of a glazed front door with a sash window on each side. The doorcase has large console brackets supporting a salient entablature with an Adam frieze of alternating anthemion and lily flower motifs.

Scale: $7\frac{1}{2}$ in. to 10 ft.

Pen and ink 315 x 460

OPH 428–1949

Prov.: Osterley Park.

Presumably a design for the door to the entrance hall, from the courtyard. Not used in execution.

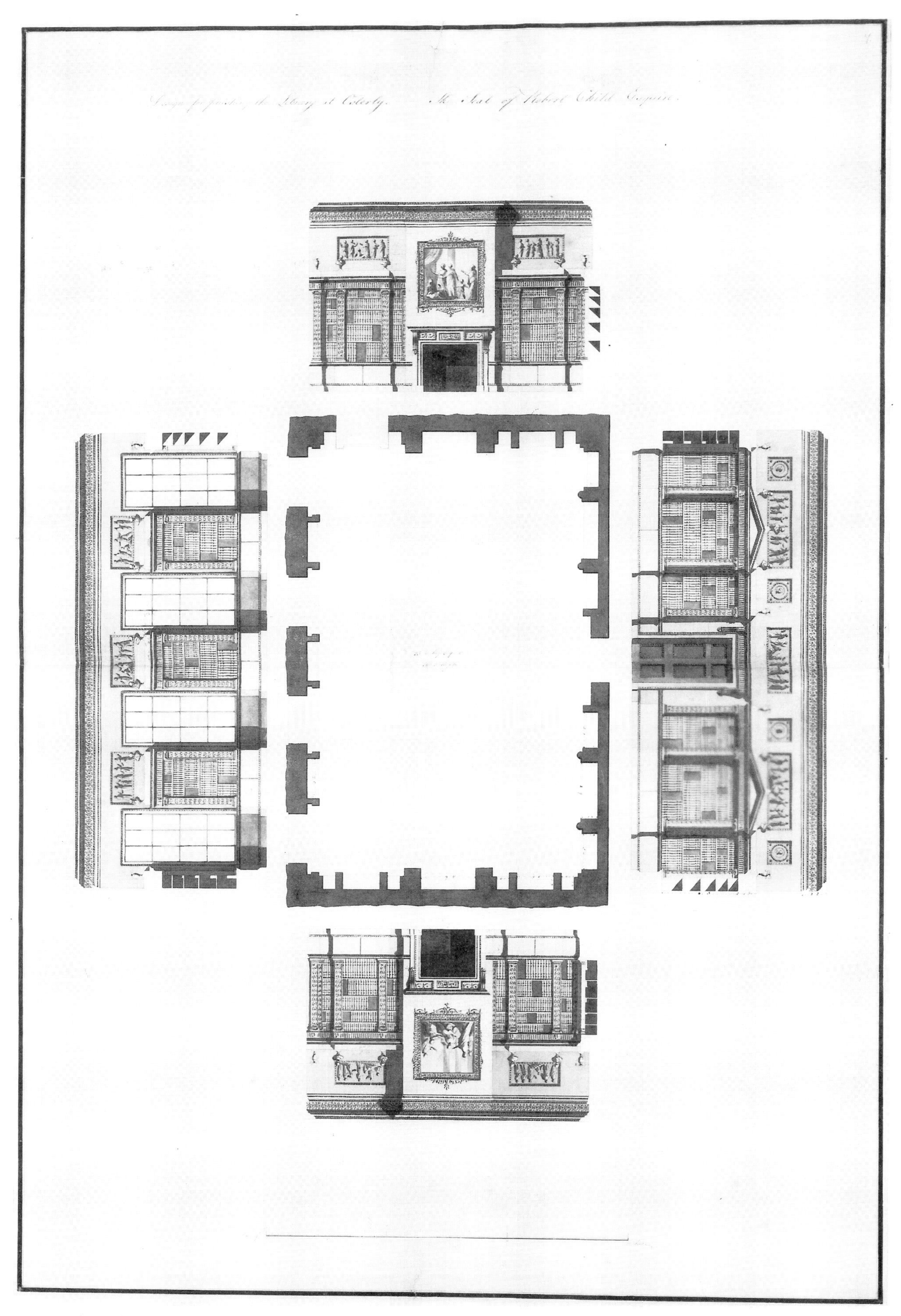

PLATE 38 (cat. 84)

PLATE 39 (cat. 85)

Designs for the completion of the interior of Osterley House including the Library (4 sheets), the Entrance Hall (3 sheets), the Dining room (2 sheets), the Drawing room (4 sheets), with various other designs.

84 Design for the Library. Plan and elevations of a rectangular room, 23 ft. by 39 ft., with the four walls 'folded down' and detached from the plan which is fully shown. Client's drawing of an elaborate neo-classical interior in which the bookcases are treated architecturally as Ionic aedicules with acroterion busts and plasterwork panels on the walls above. Paired chimneypieces at either end of the room with large neo-classical scenes set in plasterwork frames above. The chimneybreast projects well beyond the line of the bookcases. Delicate and abundant decoration of plasterwork circlets in the ceiling frieze and double guilloche on the face of the bookcase pilasters. (pl.38).

Insc. with various sizes and *Design for finishing the Library at Osterly. The seat of Robert Child Esquire.*

Pen and ink and grey washes 630x930

OPH 419–1949

Prov.: Osterley Park.

85 Design for the Library ceiling. Client's drawing of 1766. A rectangular geometric pattern of uniformly shallow relief divided into three parts by broad bands made of repeated square units – a central square with an oblong panel at either end. The centre is filled with a circular pattern radiating from an acanthus boss through flutes, Vitruvian scroll, and foliage arabesques to an outer rim of guilloche (rather inexpertly drawn). The corners of the central square are filled with semi-circular fans with free arabesques of foliage and figures. (pl. 39).

Scale: $8\frac{1}{8}$ in. to 10 ft.

Insc. in office copperplate *Design of a Cieling[sic] for the Library at Osterly. The Seat of Robert Child Esquire.* s. bottom left *Robert Adam Architect 1766.*

Pen and ink with water-colour 460x630

OPH 399–1949

Prov.: Osterley Park.

A copy of this drawing exists in the Soane Museum (S.M.D. Vol. 11, No. 202).

86 Duplicate design for the library ceiling. Copy of cat. 85 above rendered in black and white with the ceiling cornice drawn in. 1766.

Scale: $5\frac{3}{8}$ in. to 10 ft.

Insc. in office copperplate, *Design of a Ceiling for the Library at Osterley. The Seat of Robert Child Esqr/39.0 by 23.0.* s. bottom left *Robt Adam Architect* and dated *1766.*

Pen and ink and grey wash 455x615

OPH 417–1949

Prov.: Osterley Park.

PLATE 40 (cat. 87)

87 Design for the Library Chimneypiece. Client's drawing. Architectural in character with a sculpted panel on the transom of an armillary sphere flanked by putti sprouting foliage tendrils. The panel is contained by the cornice of the fireplace architrave which is checked up and over it. Console brackets to the stiles matching those of the door and a frieze, taken from that of the ceiling of the room, and not the Adamesque garlands shown in cat. 84 above. 1766. (pl. 40).

Scale: 6 $\frac{15}{16}$ in. to 5 ft.

Insc. in office copperplate *Design of a Chimney Piece for the Library at Osterly.*

Pen and ink and wash 330x450

OPH 405–1949

Prov.: Osterley Park.

A copy of this drawing exists in the Soane Museum (S.M.D. Vol. 11, No. 209). The Library at Osterley was executed essentially as it appears in these drawings: its date is usually given as c.1766. Minor differences occur in the treatment of the frieze of the bookcases which, in the room as built, matches the frieze below the ceiling cornice though in the drawing it is shown as a fluted design with acanthus leaves over the pilaster capitals. The frieze of the chimneypiece was also made to match the ceiling frieze as shown in the detailed drawing and not as in the elevations of the room. The acroterion busts and urns shown on the bookcases in the drawings are not in the room and may never have been supplied while the relief panels in the walls above were carried out not as stucco sculpture – which appears to be shown here – but as painted panels by Antonio Zucchi. One other substantial change made in the course of preparing the drawings can be used to determine the dating of the elevational scheme. These are the chimney breasts shown clearly on the drawing and present in the room but not part of the design when the scheme for the ceiling decoration, a plain rectangular area, was drawn up in 1766. In the room today, the projecting chimney breasts take up four of the repeated decorative squares of the border at either end of the ceiling design which must therefore pre-date the elevational drawing. On the other hand the detailed design of the chimneypiece proposes further alterations, also executed, and it too is dated (in the Soane Museum copy drawing) to 1766. Thus all the designs must date from the same year and will have been produced in the sequence – ceiling design, wall design and chimneypiece.

Osterley library exploits in a most perfect and systematic way one of Robert Adam's most characteristic conceptions – the aedicule bookcase. The device occurring in other Adam libraries at Croome Court, Nostell Priory and Mellerstain, and in many other designs, is here used to create a room that is at once supremely architectural, yet in its overall effect light and patently refined. Adam's library designs are discussed in Stillman 1966, pp. 23 and 87–89.

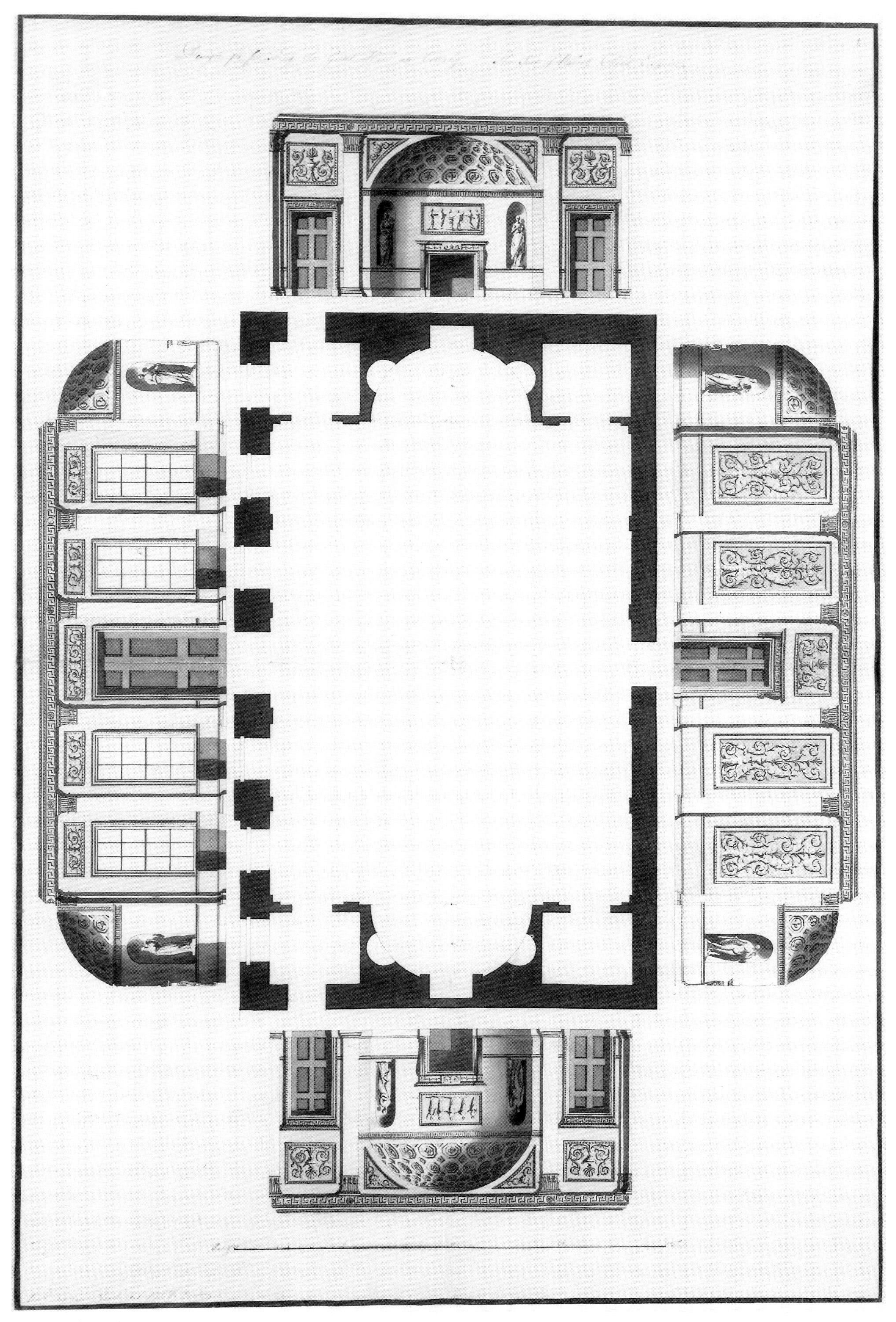

PLATE 41 (cat. 88)

PLATE 42 (cat. 89)

88 Design for the Entrance Hall. Client's drawing. Plan and elevations of a rectangular room 33 ft. by 46 ft. with a semi-circular apse, 15 ft. in diameter, flanked by rectangular cupboards or lobbies at either end. The apses each contain a central fireplace with semi-circular statue niches on each side and are roofed by shallow segmental domes. The elevations, detached from the walls of the plan and 'folded down', are articulated by 'Diocletian' pilasters, five bay on the long walls and three bay at each end. An unorthodox shallow frieze with a Greek key motif sits directly on the capitals without any architrave. Foliage arabesque panels of plasterwork in rectangular frames occupy the spaces between the pilasters, and above the windows and doors. The apses have octagonal and diamond shaped coffering. 1767. (pl. 41).

Scale: $3\frac{1}{8}$ in. to 10 ft.

Insc. with dimensions of the room and in office copperplate. *Design for finishing the Great Hall at Osterly. The Seat of Robert Child Esquire.* s. bottom left *Robt Adam Architect* and dated *1767*.

Pen and ink and grey washes 960x630

OPH 397–1949

Prov.: Osterley Park.

89 Design of the Entrance Hall ceiling. Client's drawing. A compartmented design with shallow plasterwork 'beams' of double guilloche bands continuing the visual grid of the pilasters as rectangular panels round the edge of the ceiling. The centre is a large oblong filled with a pattern of radiating oval borders. 1767. (pl. 42)

Scale: 7 in. to 10 ft.

Insc. in office copperplate. *Design of a Ceiling for the Great Hall at Osterly – The seat of Robert Child Esqr*. s. bottom left *Robert Adam Architect* and dated *1767*.

Pen and ink and grey washes 475x620

OPH 396–1949

Prov.: Osterley Park.

A copy of this drawing, replacing the martial trophies in some of the panels by a boy in rinceaux is in the Soane Museum (S.M.D. Vol. 11, no. 203). The overall pattern may be seen as a neo-classical refinement of a traditional Palladian conception going back through Ware to Lord Burlington, Jones and ultimately to sixteenth-century Venice. In the context of Adam's entire room the old formula is here given a startling modernity.

90 Design for the Entrance Hall Chimneypiece. Client's drawing. A lugged architrave frame to the fireplace with a central plaque above with patera and garlands. Stiles and frieze decorated with guilloche. 1768.

Scale: $1\frac{7}{16}$ in. to 1 ft.

Insc. *Design of a Chimney Piece for the Hall at Osterly*, and with an erased pencil inscription.

Pen and ink and grey wash 330x482

OPH 408–1949

Prov.: Osterley Park.

A copy of this drawing is in the Soane Museum (S.M.D. Vol. 22, No. 211). Like the Library, the Hall at Osterley was executed essentially as it appears in the drawings with only minor alterations of details. As in the Library Adam replaced the chimneypieces shown in the room elevations of 1767, which had console bracketed stiles, by a more delicate and flatter design of 1768. In execution the pattern of the oval rosettes of the ceiling was made more delicate to accord with the acanthus medallion of its centre and the martial trophies were removed to the plasterwork panels on the walls facing the entrance where, enlarged and on a grander scale, they replaced the foliage arabesques shown in the drawing. In keeping with this trend towards enrichment with refinement the Greek key motif of the room is more elaborate than in the drawing though Adam's scrupulous attention to the direction in which it runs, changing on each pilaster and at the centre of each bay, is carried through in the finished room. Oddly, though the tendency of the later 1760s was to match room, door and chimneypiece friezes, in the hall all are different though the drawing of 1767 shows the frieze above the door as a match for the Greek key of the room. No drawing is recorded for the floor, a design whose composition mirrors that of the ceiling without copying its detail.

91 Design for the Dining Room. Client's drawing of a rectangular room 23 ft. by 34 ft. with the four interior elevations 'folded down' from the outline of the plan. A three-bay window wall, with oval mirrors between, faces the fireplace with a panel of plasterwork arabesques on either side and mahogany doors in the corner. Panel paintings of Classical subjects surmount the chimneypiece and the doors. The end walls have large central panels of Classical ruins flanked by doors with *sopra porte* at one end, and by arabesque panels at the other. The chimneypiece is Doric with triglyph frieze and columns for the stiles. The doors are six panel designs with flat entablatures supported on shallow console brackets. (pl. 43).

Scale: $3\frac{1}{4}$ in. to 10 ft.

Insc. with dimensions and in office copperplate, *Design for finishing the Eating Parlour at Osterly. The Seat of Robert Child Esqr.*

Pen and ink and grey washes 715x510

OPH 398–1949

Prov.: Osterley Park.

92 Elevation of the Dining Room sideboard. A long rectangular design, transitional in style, supported on four straight baluster legs with lotus and block 'capitals' and fluted ball feet. The transom of the table is fringed with enclosed pendant anthemia and alternates a simple patera with a Greek key motif. Ram's heads are placed above each leg. 1767.

Scale: $\frac{3}{16}$ in. to 1 ft.

Insc. in office copperplate, *Design of a Table Frame for the side Board in the Eating Room at Osterly for Robert Child Esqr*. s. bottom left *Robert Adam Architect* and dated *1767*.

Pen and ink and wash 390x600

OPH 400–1949

Prov.: Osterley Park.

This sideboard appears incorrectly as part of the furniture of Sion House in Plate IX of the last volume of Adam 1773 published posthumously in 1822. It is discussed by Eileen Harris (1963) p. 67.

The decoration of the Dining Room at Osterley was probably done in two stages: first the ceiling for which no drawings survive though it is actually a duplicate of that in the dining room at Shardeloes designed in 1761 (see Stillman 1966, p. 69) and later the walls as recorded here. The only dated drawings for the room are those of the sideboard of 1767 and a drawing in the Soane Museum for the curtain boxes of 1768 (S.M.D. Vol. 17, No. 105). It seems unlikely that the ceiling which is comparatively coarse and not unlike that proposed for the drawing room at Mamhead should be of the same date and by the same craftsmen as the refined arabesques of the walls. The fact that its cornice appears in the drawing of the walls of the room in the conventional architect's shorthand of a line with slant corners – unlike the drawings of other room interiors for Osterley – strongly supports the view that it was already completed when the designs for the walls were made.

In execution the Doric frieze of the chimneypiece was replaced by a tablet with arabesques and the whole was heightened, altering considerably the proportions of the painted panel by Antonio Zucchi above. Zucchi's ruin pieces at either end of the room are his first known work in England for Adam and are signed and dated 1767.

93 Design for the Drawing Room. Client's drawing for a rectangular room, 23 ft. by 33 ft. 9 in., with the walls 'folded down' and detached from the plan which is fully shown. A three-bay window wall faces the fireplace with doors in the corners at either side. A door in each end wall, standard six panel type with fluted architraves, console brackets and a central plaque with winged griffins. Modillion room cornice, Vitruvian scroll chair rail and carved skirting moulding.

Scale: $\frac{3}{8}$ in. to 1 ft.

Pen and ink and wash 600x825

OPH 420–1949

Prov.: Osterley Park.

94 Design for the Drawing Room Chimneypiece. Client's drawing. Elevation of a design closely similar to cat. 93 above, with a sculpted panel on the transom showing a circular plaque of an urn flanked by winged griffons whose tails become foliage tendrils. The panel is contained by the cornice moulding of the fireplace architrave which is checked up and over it. Console brackets to the stiles spring from rams' head motifs. (pl. 44).

Scale: $1\frac{1}{2}$ in. to 1 ft.

Insc. in office copperplate, *Design of a Chimney Piece for the Drawing Room at Osterly.*

Pen and ink and grey washes 335x490

OPH 406–1949

Prov.: Osterley Park.

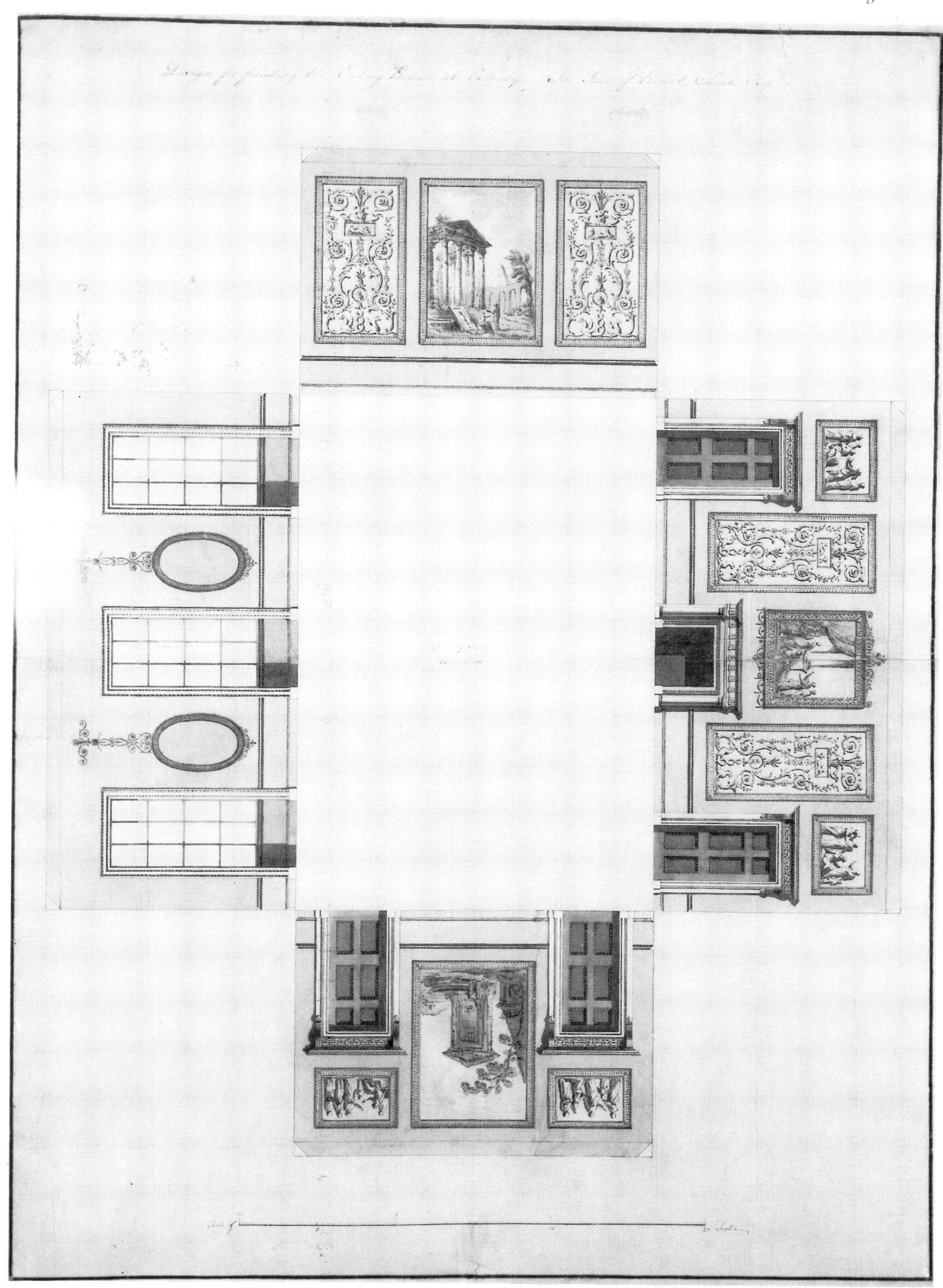

PLATE 43 (cat. 91)

PLATE 44 (cat. 94)

95 Design for the Drawing Room grate and fender. Client's drawing of a free standing basket grate with semi-circular backplate decorated with a medallion of two Classical figures. A fretwork of free-standing anthemia in ovals is much used on the grate base and for the fender. The outline of the fireplace opening is marked as a line. (pl. 45).

Scale: $\frac{3}{8}$ in. to 1 ft.

Insc. in office copperplate, *Design of a Grate for the Drawing Room at Osterly.*

Pen and ink 460x335

OPH 415–1949

Prov.: Osterley Park.

96 Design of a pier glass for the Drawing Room. Client's drawing. Elevation of a rectangular frame to sit directly on the chair rail. The top with winged griffons at the corners and seated female figures flanking an urn with arabesques of foliage sprouting from its top. Symmetrical husk garlands, whose drops frame the sides of the mirror, hang from the arabesque. 1773. (pl. 46).

Scale: $1\frac{3}{16}$ in. to 1 ft.

Insc. in office copperplate, *Design of a Glass Frame for the Drawingroom at Osterly* and dated *July 21st 1773.*

Pen and ink and grey wash with water-colour 475x310

OPH 416–1949

Prov.: Osterley Park.

97 Design for the Drawing Room Carpet. Client's drawing. A rectangular pattern, with floral motifs in circular garlands reflecting the coffers of the ceiling above. The centre is a large oval medallion framed in a rectangular border and the edge has a broad border of rosettes in diamond frames with a beaded outer and inner edge. (pl. 47).

Scale: $\frac{3}{4}$ in. to 1 ft.

Insc. in office copperplate, *Design of a Carpet for Robert Child Esqr.*

Pen and ink and watercolour 455x625

OPH 418–1949

Prov.: Osterley Park.

The Drawing Room at Osterley was probably designed in the late 1760s following the completion of the Hall and Dining Room. None of the drawings at Osterley or in the Soane Museum is dated apart from the design for the pier glasses of July 1773 by which time the room was already finished and open to visitors (see Stillman 1966, p. 72). The Osterley drawings lack only the design for the ceiling to complete the description of this opulent interior which, as with the drawings for the other rooms, reproduces the detailed drawings exactly while making slight changes from the wall elevation design which is presumably the earliest, cat. 93. In this drawing the room frieze is of free acanthus scrolls, replaced in execution by an anthemion set inside a repeated arch pattern, while the chimneypiece was changed to match the pattern of the door cases as shown in the detailed drawing. The design of the ceiling, inspired by a plate of the coffering of the Temple of the Sun at Palmyra, is one of the most celebrated instances of Adam's borrowing from antiquity without being bound by what he borrowed. The drawing of the ceiling from the Soane Museum is reproduced here for comparative purposes. (pl. 48).

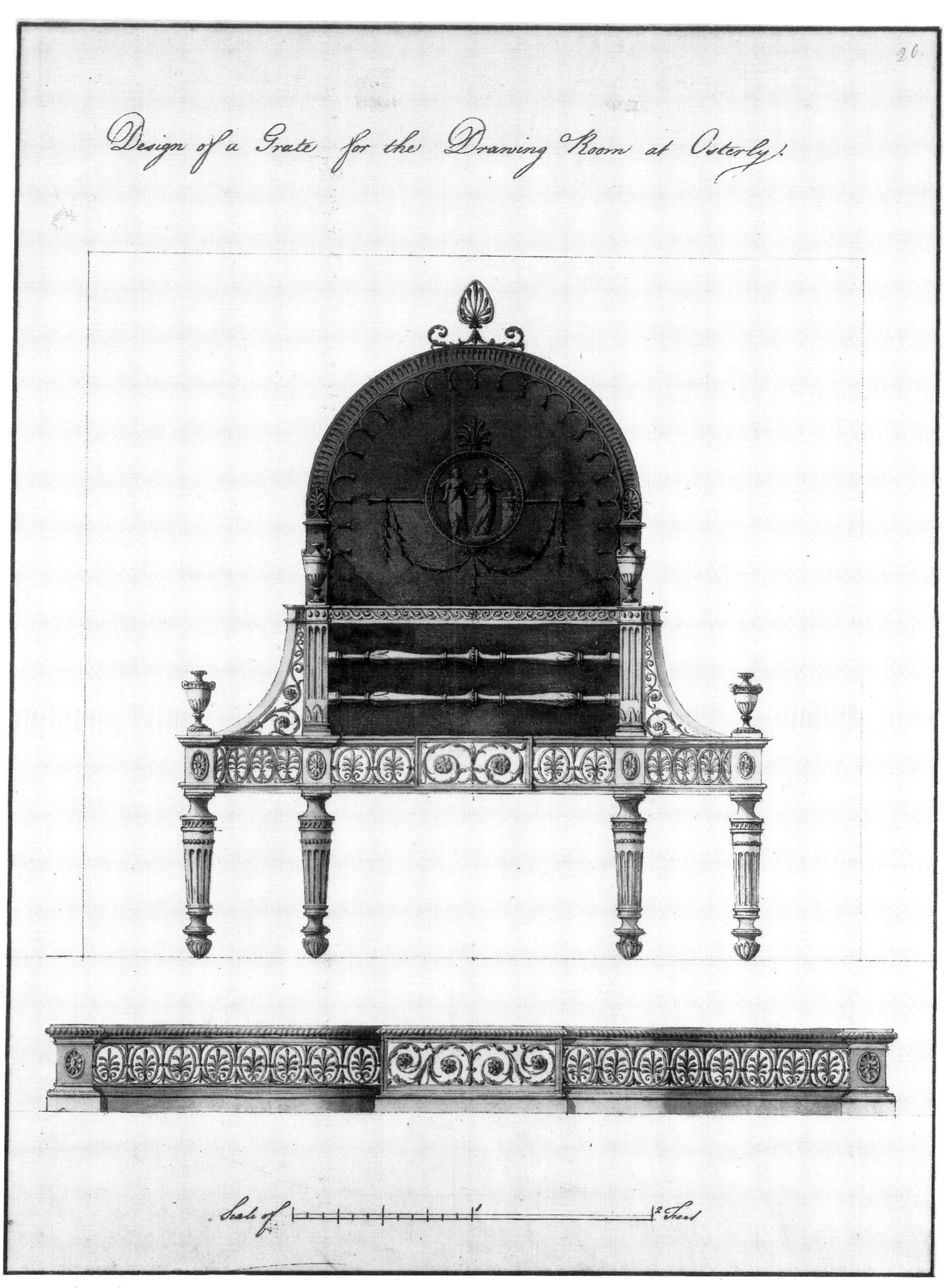

PLATE 45 (cat. 95)

PLATE 46 (cat. 96)

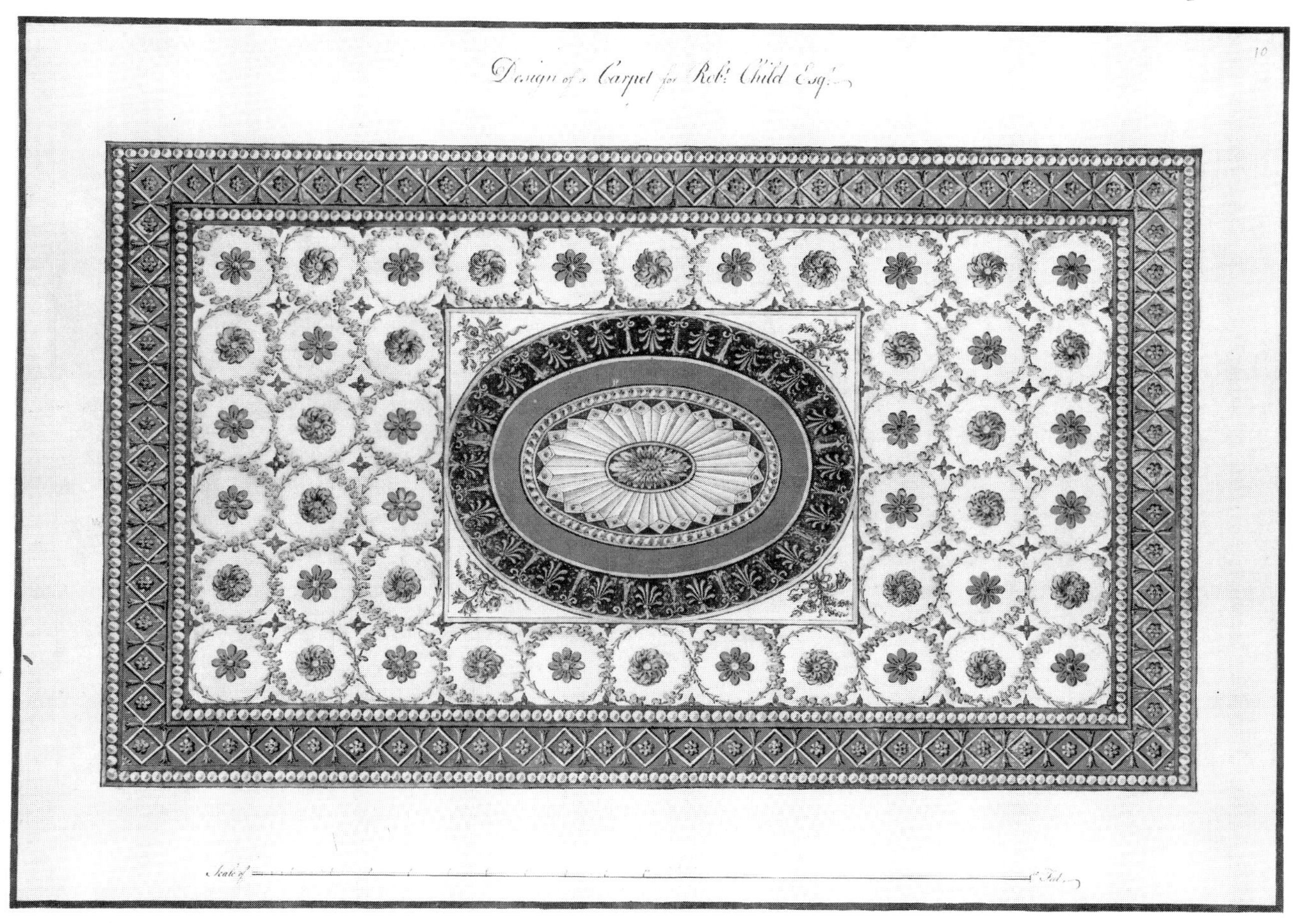

PLATE 47 (cat. 97)

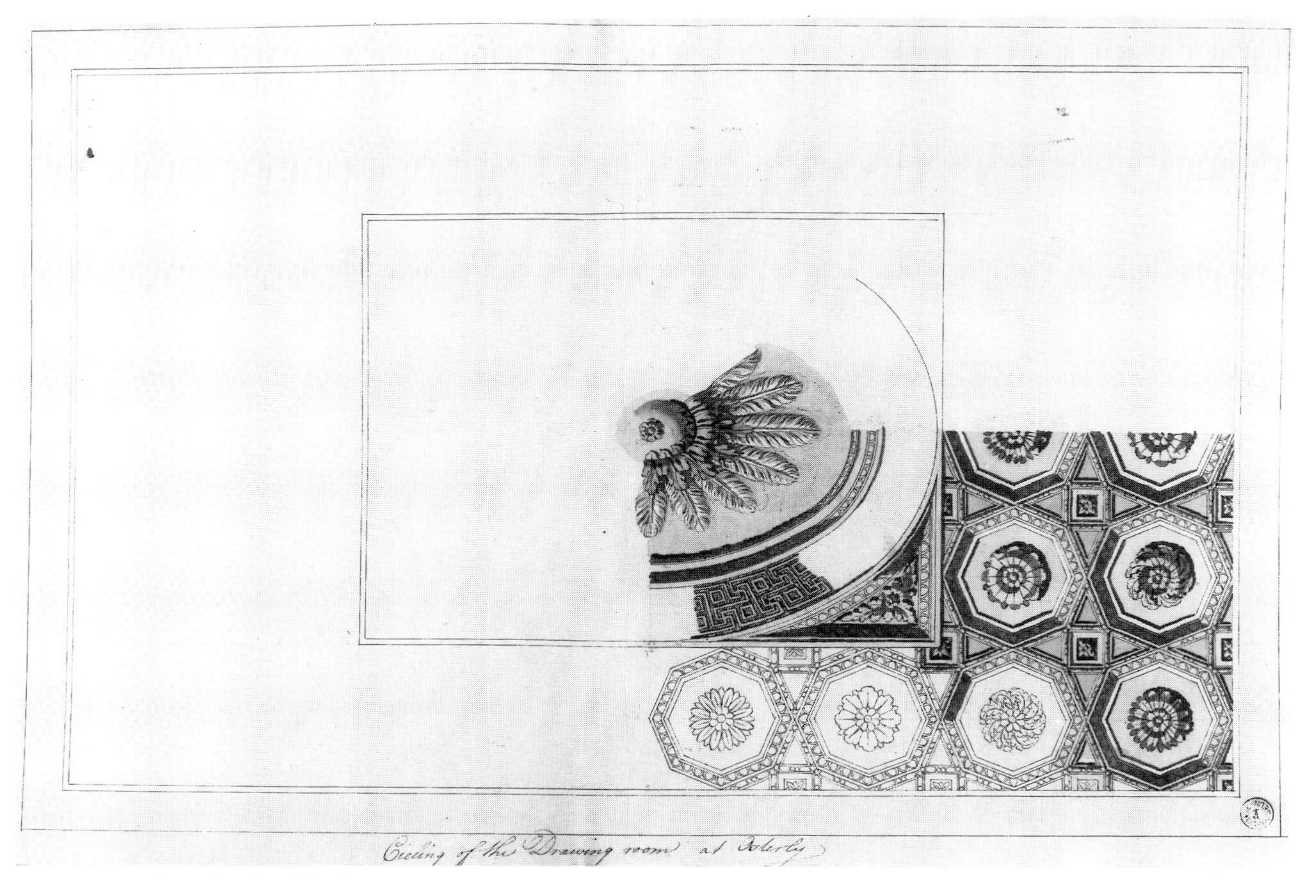

PLATE 48 Osterley Park, plan of the drawing room ceiling. (By courtesy of the Trustees of Sir John Soane's Museum.)

98 Design for the Tapestry room Chimneypiece. Client's drawing. Delicately scaled with an Adam composite pilaster order on the stiles and an entablature with inset mosaic pictures on the frieze blocks above and on the central tablet. The frieze is divided into small oval elements with cameos of heads and urns suggestive of, though not identical to, the treatment of the frieze in the room.

Scale: $1\frac{9}{16}$ in. to 1 ft.

Insc. in office copperplate, *Design of a Chimney Piece for the Tapestry Room at Osterly.*

Pen and ink wash 340x460

OPH 407–1949

Prov.: Osterley Park.

99 Design for the Bedroom Chimneypiece. Client's drawing. Delicately scaled with advanced panelled stiles with arabesque drops, the frieze blocks with rams' heads at each corner. Central plaque of a patera with crossed arms and drapery swags. The frieze alternating anthemion and lily trumpet motifs.

Scale: $\frac{5}{8}$ in. to 1 ft.

Insc. in office copperplate, *Design of a Chimney Piece for the Bed Chamber at Osterly.*

Pen and ink and wash 340x460

OPH 404–1949

Prov.: Osterley Park.

100 Design for the Dressing room Chimneypiece. Client's drawing. Elevation. A full architrave to the fireplace with narrow stiles decorated with single guilloche. The frieze blocks above with dancing putto figures. Frieze of shell fans on anthemia with foliage tendrils.

Scale: $\frac{5}{8}$ in. to 1 ft.

Insc. in office copperplate, *Design of a Chimney Piece for the Dressing Room at Osterly.*

Pen and ink and wash 335x460

OPH 427–1949

Prov.: Osterley Park.

101 Preliminary sketch design for the decoration of the Dressing room walls. Arabesque drops of parasols, urns, vases and tripods arranged about a central motif on an 'Etruscan' roundel with a long rectangular tablet above it. Paired winged sphinxes flank the roundel, with their backs to it, and below is a large tripod or incense burner supported by standing figures of satyrs. On a level with the satyrs are Vesica shaped 'Etruscan' panels each decorated with a single figure. These stand on tall plinths with ram's head and medallion decorations. The base is supplied by an alternating anthemion and lily trumpet motif. (pl. 49).

Pen and sepia ink with pencil 215x148

3436.41

Prov.: C. J. Richardson.

This drawing records an early proposal by Adam for the arabesques in the Etruscan dressing room. The upper section, from the canopies above the vesica-shaped panels, is virtually identical to a preparatory sketch in the Soane Museum, dated 11 Oct. 1775 (S.M.D. Vol. 50, No. 71). The lower portion proposes a heavier treatment that was not to be used in the design as executed where the black vesicas are replaced by slender amphorae and dancing girls take the place of the satyr figures. The whole design in the room is looser and more open than appears in the architect's first sketches. While Adam related the idea of the Etruscan room specifically to motifs in Greek vases – from which the uses of black, white and terracota is also derived – Professor Stillman believes that the mood of the wall decoration is clearly influenced by Piranesi's designs (see Stillman 1966, pp. 75–76).

Designs for buildings in the park at Osterley including a gate lodge (1 sheet), a conservatory (1 sheet), a bridge (4 sheets) and a ruined castle (1 sheet).

102 Plan and Elevation for the Gate Lodges. Client's drawing. Two lodges each 14 ft. square with pyramid roofs and central chimneys – vaulted inside – flank an arrangement of railings and gates between two plain gate piers with chamfered tops and lamps. The lodges have single windows with a flat, fluted entablature; and a fluted main frieze and cornice blocked in the centre with a garlanded plaque. 1777. (pl. 50).

Scale: $2\frac{9}{16}$ in. to 10 ft.

Insc. with dimensions and in office copperplate, *Elevation of a Gate and Lodges for Osterly Park, one of the Seats of Robert Child Esquire/Extends 60 feet.*

Pen and ink and grey wash 590x455

OPH 421–1949

Prov.: Osterley Park.

A duplicate outline drawing of this scheme is in the Soane Museum dated 15 May 1777 (S.M.D. Vol. 51, No. 104). This is lightly marked in pencil to suggest alternative treatments including a wall in place of the side gates, a higher gate pier and a dome instead of the pyramid roof of the lodges. Adam also proposed pyramid roofed lodges at Saltram in Devon and was to reuse this design in all its essentials as a proposal for lodges at Mistley, Norfolk in 1782 (see S.M.D. Vol. 51, No. 67).

103 Plan and elevation for a Conservatory. Client's design drawing. A semi-circular glazed wall is treated as five overlapping Palladian windows and capped by a garlanded frieze, cornice and balustraded parapet. It is set against plain masonry wings with pedestals and sphinxes at balustrade level. The roof is glazed as a pointed cone. Heating flues and a privy(?) in the wall behind. (pl. 51).

Scale: $\frac{1}{4}$ in. to 1 ft.

Insc. in rough copperplate, *Design of a Greenhouse for Robert Child Esqr at Osterly.*

Pen and ink and wash 418x572

OPH 409–1949

Prov.: Osterley Park.

The conservatory as executed is simpler than what is shown here lacking the pointed roof and sphinxes.

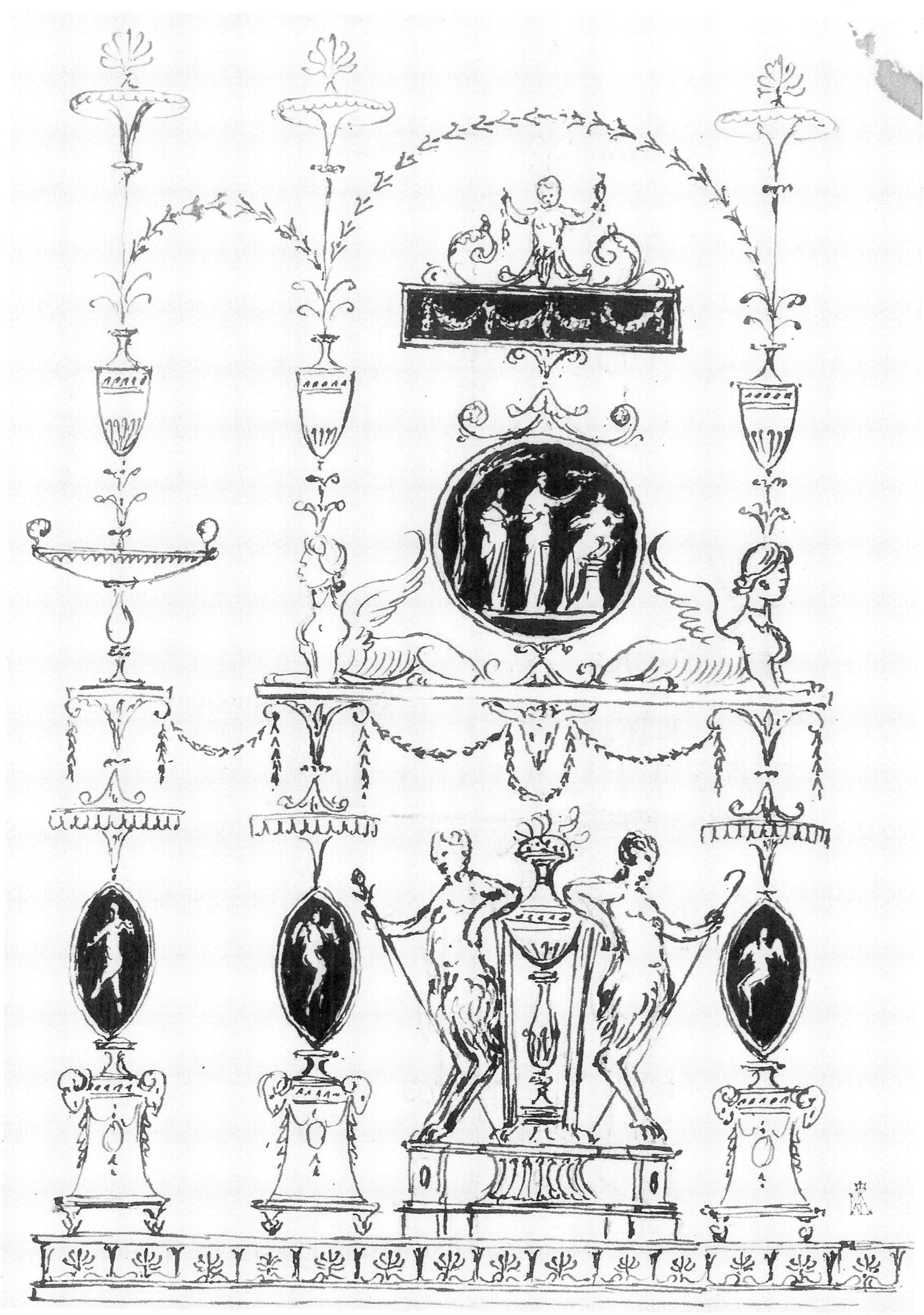

PLATE 49 (cat. 101)

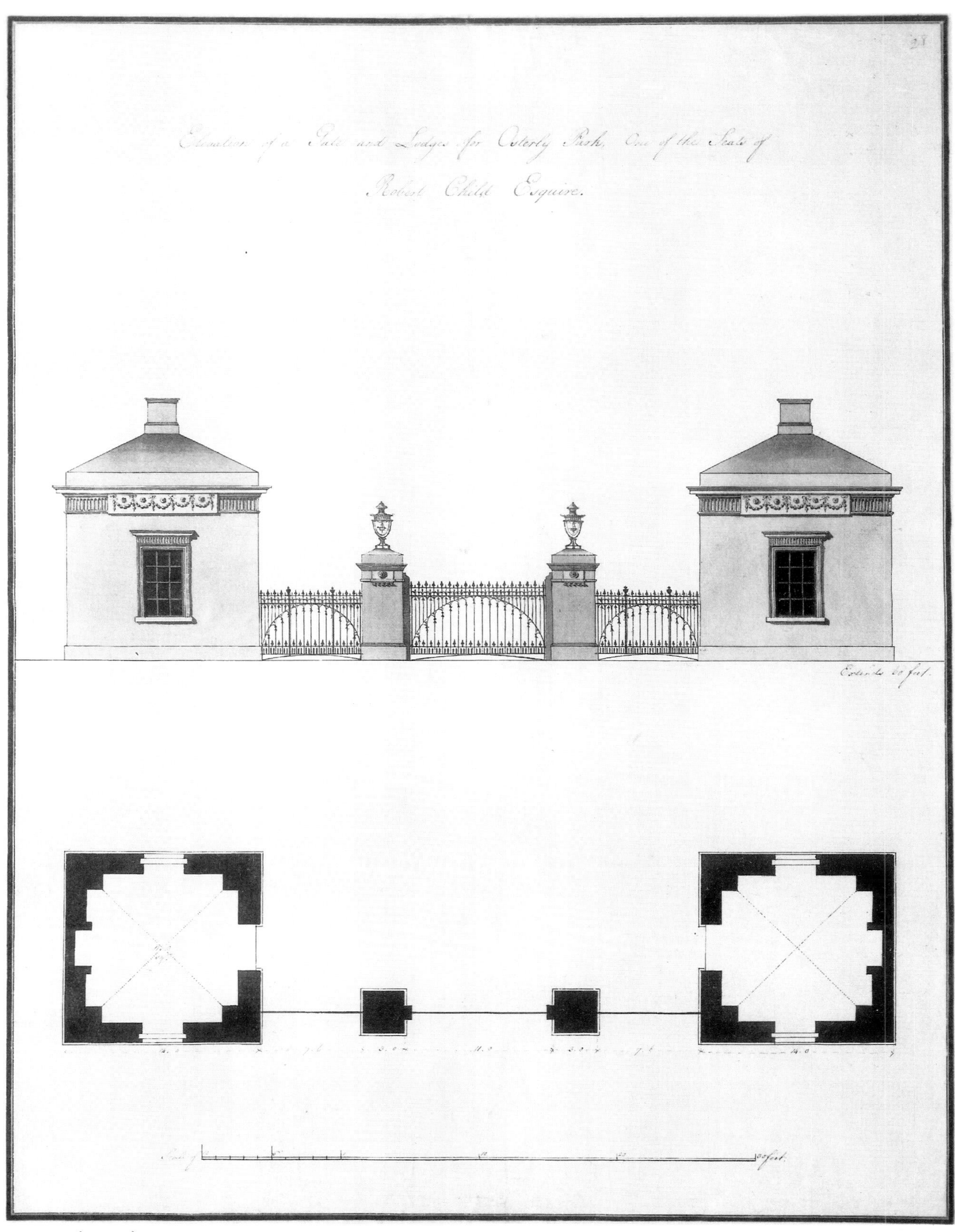

PLATE 50 (cat. 102)

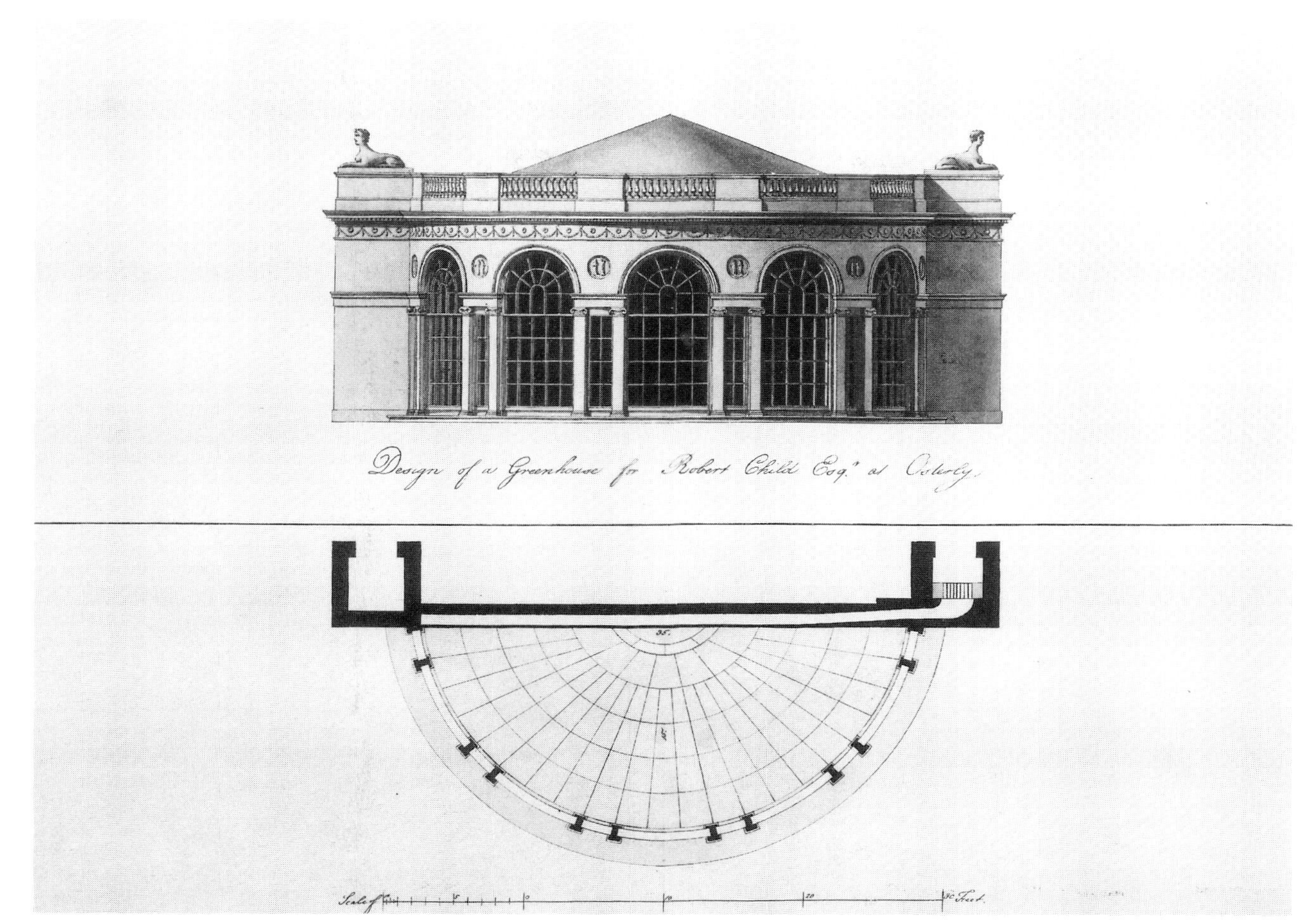

PLATE 51 (cat. 103)

104 Plan of a Bridge. Client's design drawing cut to show two levels with the plan of the piers to the left and of the parapets and balustrade to the right.
Scale: $\frac{1}{5}$ in. to 1 ft.
Insc. in office copperplate, *Plan of the Foundations/Plan of the Coach and Foot Ways.*
Pen and ink and wash 440 x 1463
OPH 428A–1949
Prov.: Osterley Park.

105 Elevation of a Bridge. Client's drawing. A design with three segmental arches, the centre wider and therefore shallower in pitch than the outer two. The piers have plain statue niches with oblong panels of foliage arabesques above and urns above the parapet. Circular sculpted reliefs in the spandrels.
Scale: $\frac{3}{16}$ in. to 1 ft.
Insc. with dimensions and in office copperplate, *Design of a Bridge for Osterly Park in Middlesex. The Seat of Robert Child Esquire/Extends 186 Feet 6 ins.*
Pen and ink and grey wash 445 x 1470
OPH 403–1949
Prov.: Osterley Park.

106 Alternative Plan for a Bridge. Client's drawing cut to show two levels with the plan of the piers on the left and the parapets and balustrade on the right. 1768. (pl. 52).
Scale: $\frac{3}{16}$ in. to 1 ft.
Insc. with span dimensions and in office copperplate, *Plan of the Foundations/Plan of Coach and Foot Ways/Whole extends[?]*; s. bottom left *Robert Adam Architect* and dated 1768.
Pen and ink and wash 389 x 1241
OPH 428B–1949
Prov.: Osterley Park.

107 Alternative Bridge elevation. Client's design drawing. A long three arched elevation with low segmental spans – that in the centre wider and therefore flatter than the others. The piers with an Adam order of pedimented aedicules framing free-standing urns. The plinths, at parapet level above, have sphinxes at either end and sea horses with putti over the central arch piers. 1768. (pl. 53).
Scale: $\frac{3}{16}$ in. to 1 ft.
Insc. with heights and in office copperplate, *Design of a Bridge for Osterly Park in Middlesex. The Seat of Robert Child Esquire*; s. bottom left *Robert Adam Archt* and dated *1768*.
Pen and ink and grey wash 395 x 1205
OPH 402–1949
Prov.: Osterley Park.

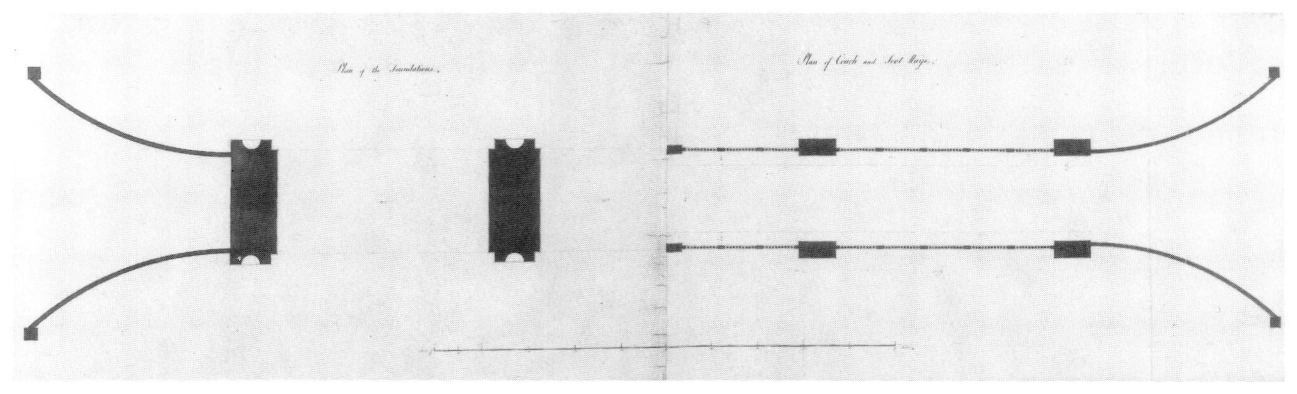

PLATE 52 (cat. 106)

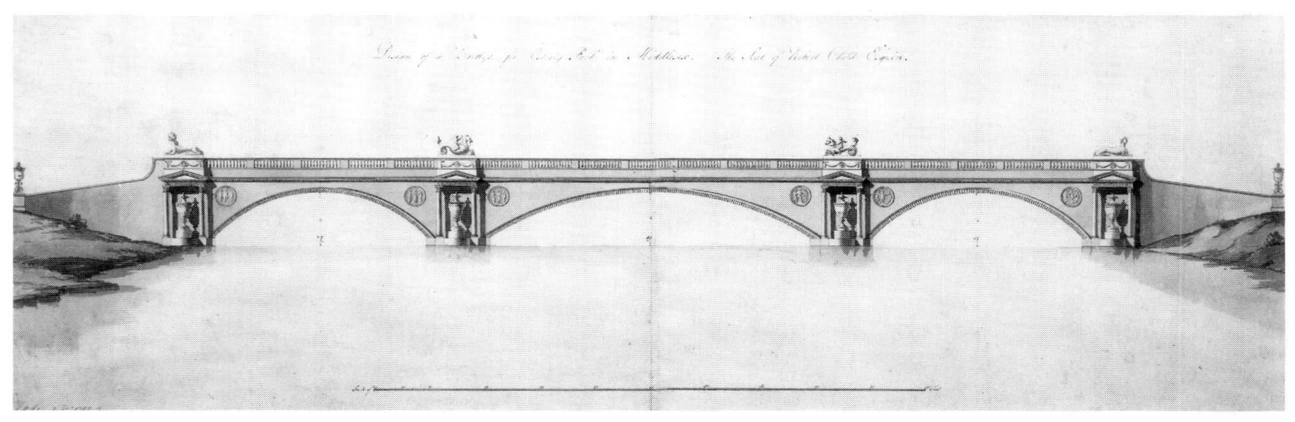

PLATE 53 (cat. 107)

The rather flat and open countryside in which Osterley stands does not lend itself to the type of bridge cum landscape feature which Adam proposes here. The central spans proposed of 39 and 60 feet hardly made the bridge an economic proposal and neither design was built. Outline copy drawings are in the Soane Museum (S.M.D. Vol. 51, Nos. 6, 7 and 8). Bolton 1922, Vol. 1, p. 300, illustrates the much smaller and heavily rusticated design which replaced these schemes.

108 Design for a Ruined Castle. Perspectival elevation of a group of ruined buildings in the Adam castle style shown in a landscape setting. The group is dominated by a large round tower with big round-headed openings and continuous machicolation at the wall head. It is linked by ranges of partly ruined walls to an enclosure defended by various interval towers – square, round and polygonal – and is approached by a round-headed archway and bridge flanked by miniature towers. Freely-painted landscape foreground with bushes and Italianate figures. 1774. (pl. 54).

Scale: $\frac{1}{8}$ in. to 1 ft.

Insc. in Robert Adam's hand(?), *Remains of the Old Castle of Osterly in Middlesex, one of the Seats of Robert Child Esqr*.

s. bottom left *Robert Adam* and dated *1774*.

Pencil, pen and ink and wash with water-colour

440 x 592

OPH 401–1949

Prov.: Osterley Park.

No other record remains of this late proposal by Adam to complete the ensemble at Osterley with the construction of an imaginary fortified precursor for the house. The style of the figures, of the landscape painting and of the architecture of the castle itself is, in each case, typical of Robert Adam himself. Even more than the Neo-Classical decorations devised for the interior of the house, the castle style was Adam's own invention and depended for its development and display entirely on the architect himself. With a scheme of this character an office clerk would have nothing to contribute, or at least not before working drawings had to be prepared. Unlike the other client's drawings for Osterley the design for the Remains of the old Castle must be largely Adam's own work and indeed this type of pictorial elevation, where a conventional architectural drawing is changed into a quasi view was a mode of display which he particularly favoured for his castle projects, where the novelty of composition and style might otherwise confuse a client. Pencil lines behind the towers to the right suggest that, despite its haphazard appearance, the elevation has been constructed from a plan.

As so often happens in Adam's work this design for one client, which was to remain unbuilt, introduces a number of themes that were to remain in the back of the architect's mind and were to reappear later in other proposals. The round tower, with its continuous machicolation, becomes a feature in his later castle style houses – Dalquharran, Culzean, Pitfour and in schemes for Blair Drummond and Castle Semple – while this particular

PLATE 54 (cat. 108)

tower, dumpy, solid and itself surely a derivative from Theodoric's mausoleum at Ravenna (which Adam had drawn with Clérisseau in 1755), was to reappear as the Mausoleum to David Hume in the Calton Hill burying ground in Edinburgh in 1777 and a year later as a tea house at Auchencruive in Ayrshire (cf. S.M.D. Vol. 19, Nos. 76–78 and 84; and 159–162). Similarly the battlemented gateway reappears – at least in idea – in the battlemented triumphal arch that opens into the forecourt of Culzean Castle while the 'ruined' viaduct of 1780 that leads to the house represents the only instance in which the architect succeeded in having such a scheme for an old building carried into execution. For a discussion of Adam's castle style buildings see Fleming 1968 I and II, Macaulay 1975 and Rowan 1974 I and 1985.

109 Scheme of proposed alterations to Osterley, before 1756. Ground floor plan of a wide, U-shaped house, with a nine-bay front, ending in broad canted bays, and narrow seven-bay wings behind. These enclose a rectangular back court with a detached colonnaded link between the ends of the wings. Much overdrawn in pencil and ink with crude, experimental alternatives. Light hatchings on part of the north front and east wing may possibly indicate existing walls.

Insc. *Plan for the alteration of Mr Child's House at Osterley.* The use of rooms is marked *A* to *M*.

Pencil, pen and ink with wash 430x500

OPH 428D–1949

Prov.: Osterley Park.

This drawing hardly seems to relate to Osterley as it was to be rebuilt from 1756 on. The main front proposed here faces north whereas that rebuilt before Adam was called in by Francis Child faces west. The handwriting on the plan has certain similarities with that of Sir William Chambers but the likeness is not conclusive and this awkward design must remain anonymous.

PLATE 55 (cat. 110)

PLATE 56 (cat. 111)

LONDON, Hounslow (formerly Middlesex), Syon House, Isleworth

The Porter's Lodge and the Gallery, for the Earl and Duke of Northumberland

110 Elevation of the entrance side of one of the pair of square lodges on the green before the west front of Syon. A two-storey, single bay elevation with rusticated ground floor, Vitruvian Scroll string course, ashlar first floor and battlemented parapet above a simple cyma recta cornice. Doric and Ionic aedicules to the door and window. (pl. 55).

Scale: 2½ in. to 5 ft.

Insc. with some heights and *Porters Lodge for the Right Honble The Earl of Northumberland at Sion.*

Pen and ink and wash with yellow water-colour 514x355

86

Prov.: No provenance is recorded for this drawing which was purchased by the Museum 18 Dec. 1857 apparently for one shilling.

Both the inscription on this drawing and the handling are comparable with work produced in the Adam office in the early 1760s. Adam began working at Syon in 1761: this drawing must have been made before 1766 as the Earl of Northumberland was created a Duke in that year. While the style of the rustication and the string course – with its tell-tale central anthemion – is perfectly acceptable as Adam work, the aedicules themselves – with columns on elongated plinths, disporportionately small capitals and an awkward width to span – look like sixteenth- or early seventeenth-century work that Adam decided to retain. In this respect it is worth noting that no dimensions are given for the aedicules while the new rustication is sized.

111 Perspective view of the interior of the gallery, sometimes called the Library, from the break in the centre of the east front looking north. (pl. 56).

Pen and ink with water-colour 416x575

E. 1063–1940

Prov.: bought from Christie, Manson and Wood.

The identity of the draughtsman of this superb interior view of one of the Adam brothers' richest interiors is not recorded. The drawing is reproduced in Adam 1773, Vol. III, pl. 2. For a discussion of the architecture of this room see pp. 20–21.

LONDON, Richmond (formerly Surrey), Duke of Montagu's house

Plan of a garden alcove for the Duke of Montagu: 1772.

112 Plan showing an apsidal recess flanked by two small niches (for seats) and framed by free standing columns and quarter engaged pilasters.

Insc. *Plan of the Garden Seat* and added in another hand *for their Graces the Duke & Dutchess[sic] of Montague* dimensions indicated and *extends 12 Feet.*

Pen and ink and wash 475 x 502

2828

Prov.: C. J. Richardson.

This drawing is identical to the plan published in Adam 1773, Vol. II, Pl. VIII in 1778, which also shows the elevation, the drawing for which remains in the Soane Museum (S.M.D. Vol. 30, No. 121). The heavy black border and sizing in black ink with little arrows is not typical of Adam's normal office practice. Both drawings are presumably copies of the sheets that were sent to the engraver. The seat was to have contained an antique pedestal and urn the base of which appears as a grey circle on this plan.

MAMHEAD HOUSE, Devon

Plans of three alternative schemes (on 10 sheets) prepared for the first Earl of Lisburne, for the alteration and extension of an earlier house with proposals for a new north and west elevation (4 sheets), offices (2 sheets) and designs for individual rooms (8 sheets). 1766–69.

113 Basement plan: applicable to all schemes for the house. A client's drawing.

Scale: 1⅜ in. to 10 ft.

Insc. *Plan of the Cellar Story of Mamhead House* and with the dimensions and names.

Pen and ink with grey washes 617x479

D. 2169–1896

Prov.: Rimell & Son.

114 Ground floor plan of the largest scheme. Client's drawing.

Scale: 1⅜ in. to 10 ft.

Insc. *Plan of the Principal Story of Mamhead House in Devonshire, The Seat of The right Hon*[ble] *Lord Lisburne* and with dimensions and names of rooms.

Pen and ink with black ink wash 621x481

D. 2166–1896

Prov.: Rimell & Son.

115 First floor plan of the largest scheme. Client's drawing.

Insc. *Plan of the Bed Chamber Story of Mamhead House* and with dimensions and names of rooms. The sheet numbered *20*.

Pen and ink with black ink wash 615x481

D. 2167–1896

Prov.: Rimell & Son.

116 Second floor plan of the largest scheme. Client's drawing.

Scale: 1⅜ in. to 10 ft.

Insc. *Plan of the Great Story of Mamhead House* and with dimensions and names of rooms.

Pen and ink with black washes 617x472

D. 2168–1896

Prov.: Rimell & Son.

117 Ground floor plan of the smaller scheme with pencilled alterations to dining room and hall. Client's drawing. (pl. 57).

Scale: 1⅜ in. to 10 ft.

Insc. *Plan of the Principal Story of Mamhead House in Devonshire, The Seat of the Right Hon*[ble] *Lord Lisburne* and with dimensions and names of rooms.

Pen and ink with black ink wash and pencil 624x477

D. 2178–1896

Prov.: Rimell & Son.

118 First floor plan of the smaller scheme. Client's drawing.

Scale: 1⅜ in. to 10 ft.

Insc. *Plan of the Bed Chamber story of Mamhead House* and with dimensions and names of rooms.

Pen and ink with dark grey wash 632x472

D. 2179–1896

Prov.: Rimell & Son.

An inscription across the back of this drawing, added presumably when it was kept in a roll, has been erased.

119 Second floor plan of the smaller scheme. Client's drawing.

Insc. *Plan of the Garret Story of Mamhead House* and with dimensions and names of rooms.

Pen and ink with black wash 630x478

D. 2180–1896

Prov.: Rimell & Son.

120 Ground floor plan of the smallest scheme. Client's drawing.

Scale: 1⅜ in. to 10 ft.

Insc. *Plan of the Principal story of Mamhead House in Devonshire, The Seat of the Right Hon*[ble] *Lord Lisburne* and with dimensions and names of rooms. Sheet numbered *37*.

Pen and ink with black wash 624x842

D. 2184–1896

Prov.: Rimell & Son.

121 First floor plan of the smallest scheme. Client's drawing.

Scale: 1⅜ in. to 10 ft.

Insc. *Plan of the one pair of stairs story of Mamhead House in Devonshire, The Seat of the Right Hon*[ble] *Lord Lisburne* and with dimensions and names of rooms. Page numbered *36*.

Pen and ink with black wash 638x840

D. 2185–1896

Prov.: Rimell & Son.

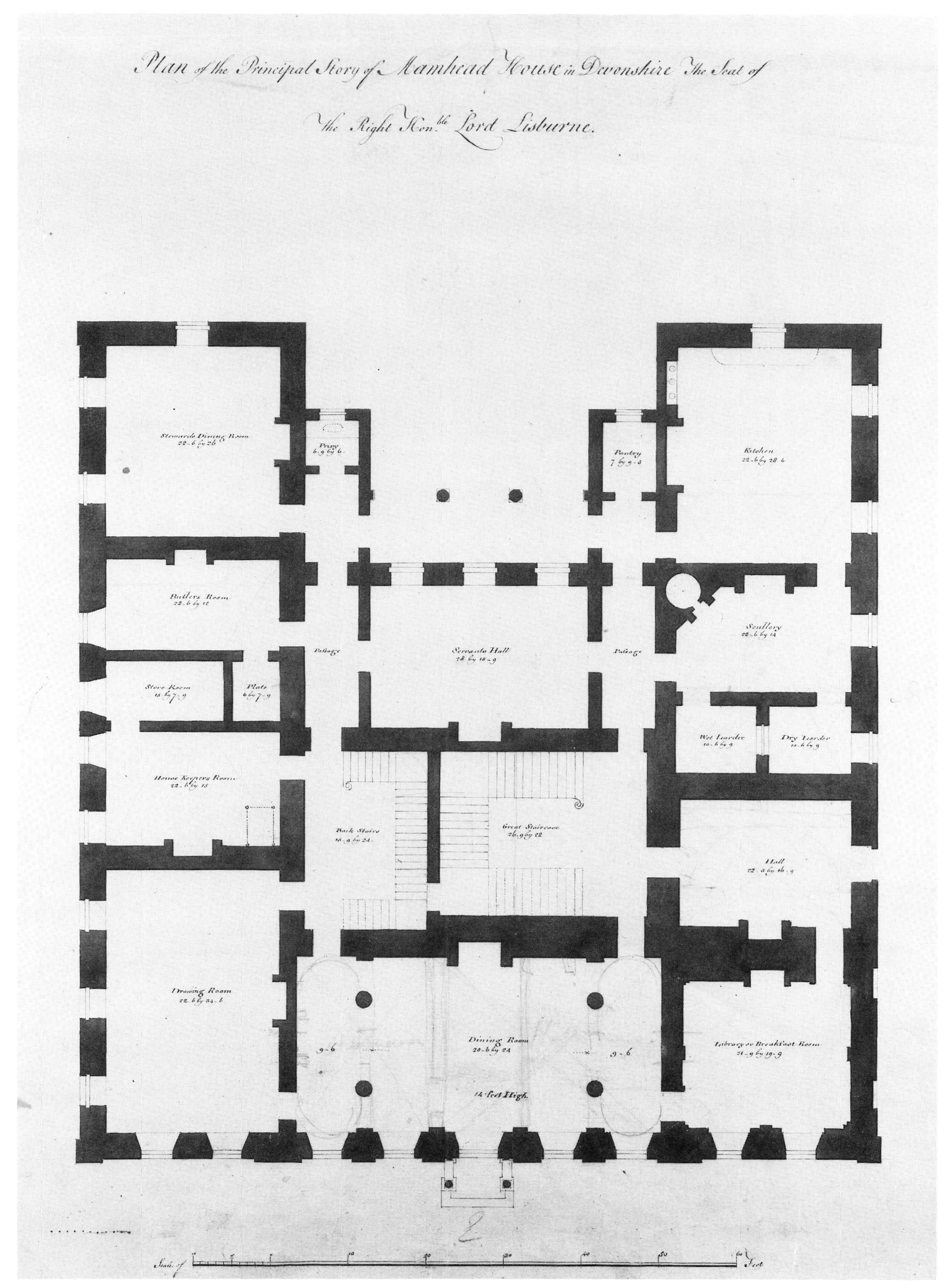

PLATE 57 (cat. 117)

122 Second floor plan of the smallest scheme. Client's drawing. This plan is limited to the north range of the house alone.

Scale: $1\frac{3}{8}$ in. to 10 ft.

Insc. *Plan of the Attic story of Mamhead House* and with dimensions and names of rooms.

Pen with black ink wash 590x448

D. 2186–1896

Prov.: Rimell & Son.

123 Rough plan of ground floor showing proposed alterations with a court behind the house. Once folded as a bundle.

Insc. with ink notes recording the use of rooms with additions in pencil that comment on what was required by the client. Insc. on the *Verso. Plan of the Ground Storey Mamhead House.*

Pen and ink

D. 2193–1896

Prov.: Rimell & Son.

124 Rough plan of first floor showing proposed alterations with a court behind the house.

Pen and ink 616x576

D. 2194–1896

Prov.: Rimell & Son.

It is possible that this drawing and the preceding plan were made by a local person and that only the pencil notes and sketched alterations were drawn by Adam.

125 North elevation for the largest scheme. Client's drawing. A plain range of three-storey building, nine bays long with corner quoin pilasters and string course moulding joining the first floor window sills. Small eaves cornice, blocking course and shallow hipped roof.

Scale: $1\frac{3}{8}$ in. to 10 ft.

Insc. *Elevation of the North Front of Mamhead House.*

Pen and ink with grey wash 474x611

D. 2165–1896

Prov.: Rimell & Son.

126 North elevation for the smaller scheme. Client's drawing. A simple classical range, three storeys by seven bays essentially the same at cat. 125 above though the facade is shorter and has gained in enrichment with moulded architraves to all the windows and flat entablatures over the ground floor windows. A door with console brackets occupies the third ground floor bay.

Scale: $1\frac{3}{8}$ in. to 10 ft.

Pen and ink with grey wash 343x508

D. 2177–1896

Prov.: Rimell & Son.

127 North elevation for the smallest scheme. Client's drawing. A regular classical facade, three storeys by seven bays like cat. 126 above though with the additional enrichment of the entablatures to the first floor windows as well as those on the ground floor. No door case on this elevation.

Scale: $1\frac{3}{8}$ in. to 10 ft.

Pen and ink with grey wash 292x500

D. 2181–1896

Prov.: Rimell & Son.

128 West or rear elevation, applicable to all schemes for the house. Client's drawing. Astylar facade, U-shaped, of three storeys with deeply recessed central section of three bays screened by a single-storey Tuscan loggia. This is contained between the narrow ends of two passages, which are themselves framed by the projecting single bay end facades of the north and south ranges. A characteristically functional Adam facade avoiding any reference to the quoin pilasters of the schemes for the north front. (pl. 58).

Scale: $1\frac{3}{8}$ in. to 10 ft.

Pen and ink with grey wash 363x519

D. 2182–1896

Prov.: Rimell & Son.

129 Second floor plan of proposed office building at Mamhead.

Scale: $1\frac{3}{8}$ in. to 10 ft.

Insc. *Plan of the Attic story of the offices for Mamhead House* and numbered *32*.

Pen and ink with grey wash 241x372

Prov.: 2187–1896.

Prov.: Rimell & Son.

Though symmetrical in itself this plan, providing for six servants' bedrooms and two stairs, was evidently intended to be built on to one end of the house.

130 The front of the offices. A balanced three-storey facade, pedimented in the centre with the windows arranged in groups of three as a plain Venetian type on the ground floor and flat headed above – a typical Adam system for giving economical emphasis to a utilitarian structure. The centre projects slightly and is flanked by plain three-bay, three-storey facades with an arcaded ground floor open on the right and blind on the left.

Insc. *Front of Offices for Mamhead House in Devonshire* and with indication of floor heights and *Extends 60 ft. 0 in.* and with rough pencil notes.

Pen and ink with grey wash 241x376

D. 2183–1896

Prov.: Rimell & Son.

Of the three schemes for Mamhead recorded in these drawings none was to be executed. Adam was later asked to supply designs for an entirely new house in 1774 and again to consider alterations in 1777 (S.M.D. Vol. 32, No. 28–34 and Nos. 21–26). No substantial work can have been done however as Mamhead is shown in 1821 in Neale (series I, Vol. 4) very much as it must have been when Adam first drew up proposals for its improvement. The house was to be demolished soon after when, in 1830, a new Elizabethan design by Anthony Salvin was started in its place. The principal front of Mamhead faced east (pl. 66) and is shown by Neale to have had an irregular five-bay, two-storey centre of late seventeenth-century character. This was articulated by a superimposed system of pilasters, Ionic on the ground floor and Corinthian or Composite above.

PLATE 58 (cat. 128)

An extra short bay without openings appeared at the north end and the first-floor windows had oval plaques or possibly mezzanine windows above them. The door was in the middle with a small porch supported by free-standing columns. On either side of this facade were plain Georgian additions, two-storey on the north and three-storey to the south. The ground floor plans of Adam's three schemes (cat. 114, 117 and 120 above) all record the essential features shown by Neale's view, (pl. 66) and these are confirmed – though possibly in a regularised form – by the office outline copy elevation of the front, preserved in the Soane Museum (S.M.D. Vol. 32, No. 21). (pl. 65). It is worth noting that as the designs were drawn up by different clerks in the brothers' London office the representation of the old front varies slightly in the different schemes (see for example the details of the porch and columns). Furthermore as these are design proposals for a client's consideration no distinction is made between pre-existing and new work as would have been the case had the commission proceeded to a working drawing stage (as for example at Compton Verney, see cat. 53 and 54 above). Any record as to the extent and layout of old Mamhead is thus limited to what may be inferred from the incidence of narrow or irregular window openings or from variations of wall thicknesses within the plan. Each plan is developed as a U-shaped complex in which the old seventeenth-century frontage fills the bottom of the 'U'. The windows across this whole facade in each scheme are narrower than the others and have splayed reveals so the whole of this front may be presumed to be kept from the original house.

The main differences in Adam's three proposals lie principally in the extent of the rebuilding that was envisaged behind this facade. The smallest and the smaller schemes retain sections of both the south and the north ranges and each proposes the retention of a large saloon – presumably pre-existing – in the centre of the old front at first floor level with a high ceiling rising into the space of the floor above. The smallest scheme economically accepts the existing top floor of the south range as its second floor plan proposal (cat. 122 above) is only concerned with the north side of the house, an addition which, if it had been made, would have balanced up the lop sided.effect of the front of the house as shown by Neale. In all the schemes Adam has redesigned the vertical circulation within the house, proposing new staircases immediately behind the old entrance hall and first floor saloon, with the service stair descending to a small basement area, whose logical layout and limited extent suggests that it was to be built without affecting the main walls of the north and south ranges. The great stairs of the smaller, and the largest designs are of three straight cantilevered flights running round three sides of a rectangle and top lit by a circular roof light. Though simple they are exactly comparable to the stairs at Ugbrooke nearby, which Adam had designed for Lord Clifford in 1763.

With a main frontage facing east and a back that enjoyed the best orientation old Mamhead was inconveniently sited: the detail of Adam's different proposals may not now be important yet it should be noted that he attempts, particularly in the largest scheme, to position the best rooms in the sunnier parts of the house. Nonetheless the servants whose hall and courtyard faced west and the steward and housekeeper with rooms on the south front seem to have done unusually well! The existence of three such similar schemes, all fully drawn up is unusual, and may be taken to mean that Adam had been asked by Lord Lisburne to make various proposals within specific cost limits. It is certainly remarkable that the largest scheme which extended the

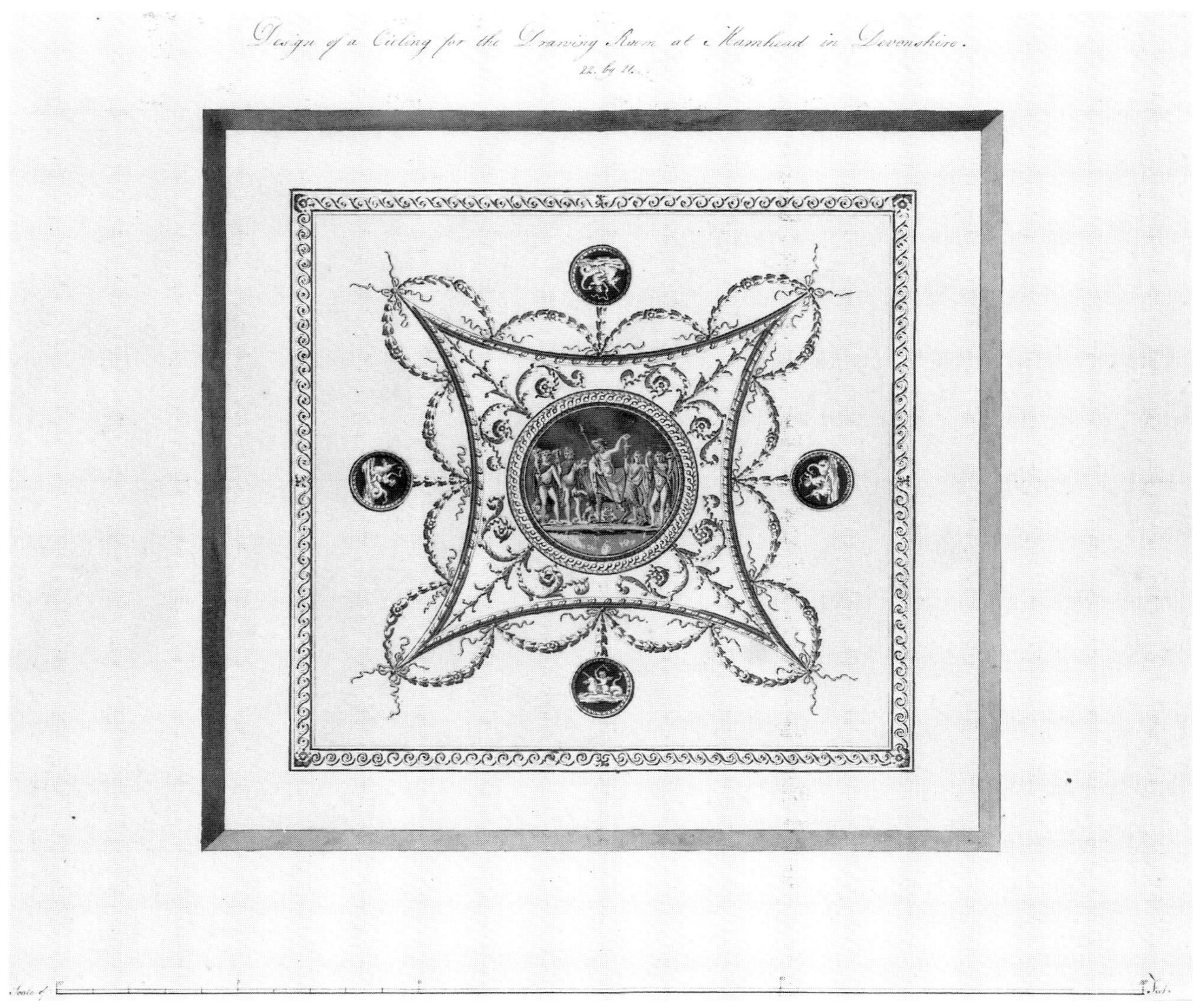

PLATE 59 (cat. 132)

north and south ranges by an extra two windows and provided much more bedroom accommodation has by far the most severe elevational treatment, and that this increases in elaboration in inverse proportion to the building work involved in any scheme. Equally with money saved on less building work the decoration proposed for the entrance hall and dining room of the smallest scheme appears to be more elaborate than in the other plans. As client's drawings each set of plans tends to show the house diagramatically rather than with architectural precision: the dimensions of rooms vary slightly from plan to plan and from those indicated in the detailed proposals for individual rooms (see below). These cannot be made to fit exactly into any particular scheme shown here. Similarly the elevations ignore the need for chimney stacks though the north range of the largest scheme required no less than eighteen flues while the western extremity in all three plans had six fireplaces, many of which from the point of view of the elevation were inconveniently sited, behind the blank windows of the outer bays. The finish of these drawings is not particularly attractive: Adam is proposing some functional improvements to tidy up an old house. A business-like approach is all that is required and the presentation drawings can be left to competent clerks in the office.

131 Design for a drawing room. Elevations of a small rectangular room, 22 ft. by 21 ft., with the four walls 'folded down' from the sides of the plan. Rich but not elaborate with a modillion cornice, deep plaster frieze, moulded chair rail and carved skirting board. Doorways with horizontal entablatures and friezes decorated with Adamesque garlands which are repeated in the transom of the chimney piece. Standard six-panel doors and a two-bay window wall with square-headed looking glass between the windows.

Scale: $2\frac{7}{8}$ in. to 5 ft.

Insc. *Section of the Drawing Room at Mamhead* and with dimensions.

Pen and ink with grey wash and water-colour 617x465

D. 2170–1896

Prov.: Rimell & Son.

The longer walls of this drawing have been cut out below the cornice level and replaced by fresh sheets of paper.

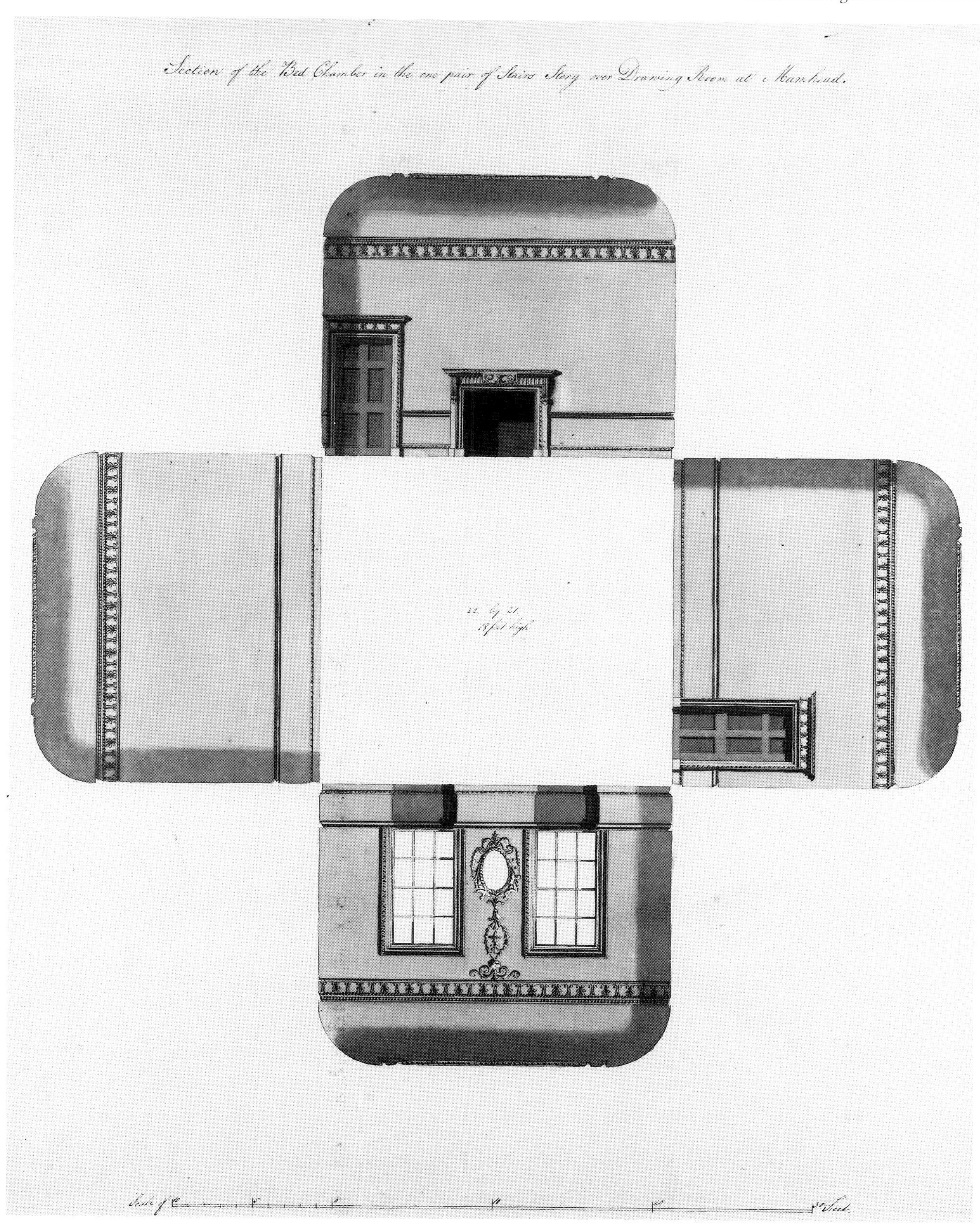

PLATE 60 (cat. 133)

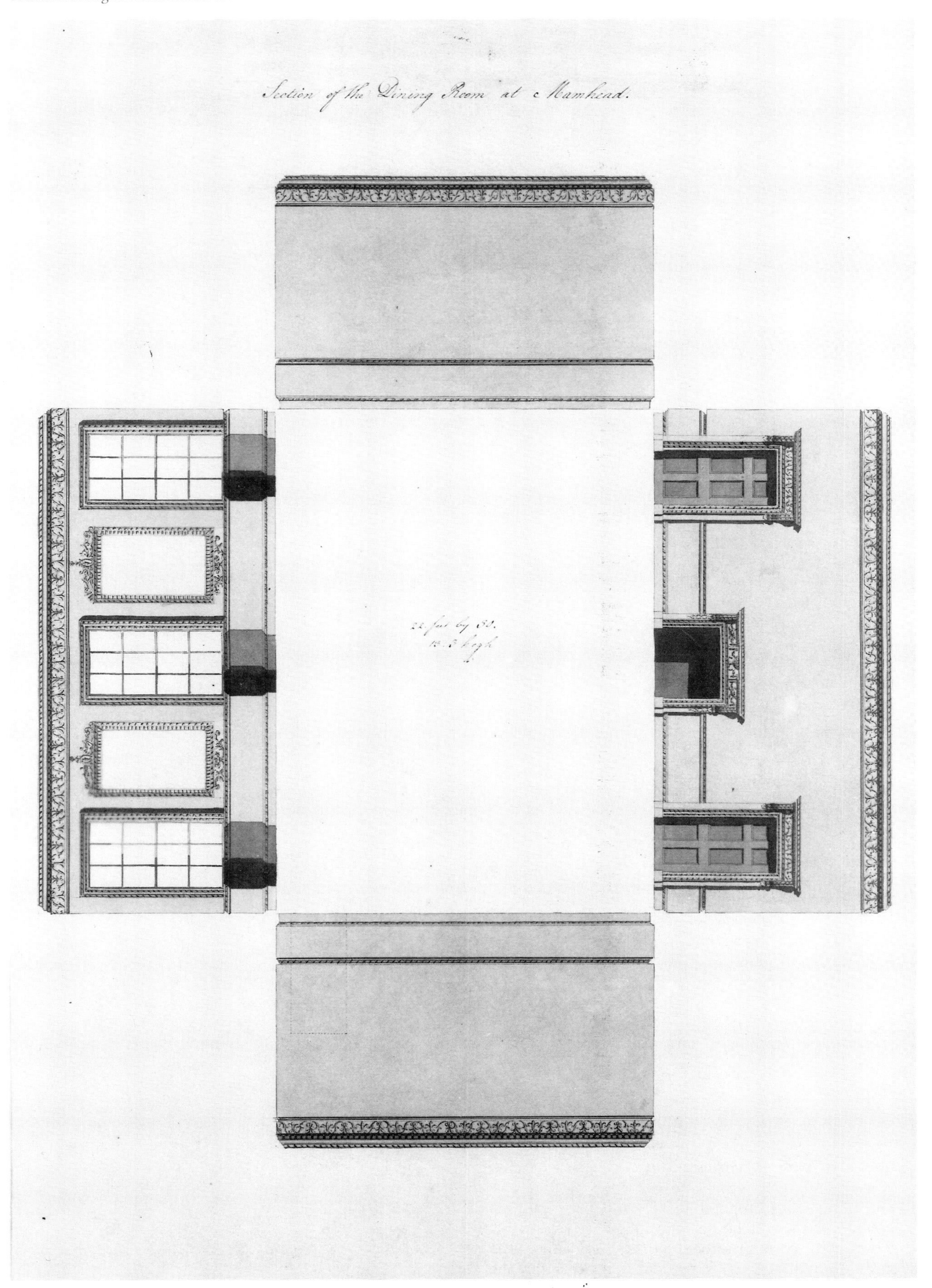

PLATE 61 (cat. 134)

PLATE 62 (cat. 135)

132 Design for a drawing room ceiling. Painted plasterwork to match cat. 131 above. A border of Vitruvian scrolls, set in some $2\frac{1}{2}$ ft. from the edge of the walls defines the decorated area of the ceiling. The centre is a large painted roundel, 4 ft. 6 in. in diameter, representing Bacchus on a Leopard. It is surrounded by a guilloche border and contained within a sharply pointed rectangle made by the intersection of four wide arcs. From the middle of each arc a medallion of a putto astride a sea horse is suspended by a garlanded rope which encircles the whole central design in a series of regularly disposed swags attached to the arcs by ribbons. (pl. 59).

Scale: $2\frac{7}{8}$ in. to 5 ft.

Insc. *Design of a Cieling[sic] for the Drawing Room at Mamhead in Devonshire. 22 ft. by 21 ft.*; numbered *11*.

Pen and ink with water-colour washes and body colour 463 x 604

D. 2171–1896

Prov.: Rimell & Son.

This room does not correspond to that in the south east corner of the survey plan (cat. 123 above). It may relate to an earlier proposal limited to the redecoration of rooms in the old house, in which case it is most likely to have been for a room on the south side of the house. Alternatively it is perhaps a scheme for the room in the north east corner of the ground floor indicated variously as a library, an ante-room or a breakfast room on the plans. This was 21 ft. 9 in. by 19 ft. 9 in., but as the wall on the north is unusually thick the room could have been extended to become the 22 by 21 ft. shown in these designs. Even if this were so the drawing of the room is still reversed from that shown on the plans. As this also occurs with other individual room designs it may perhaps be explained, though it argues a rather lax attitude in the Adam office, by a clerk being confused as to which side of a sheet of paper should be drawn up on the basis of an outline that had been 'pricked through' from another plan.

133 Bedroom design. Elevations of a rectangular room, 22 ft. by 21 ft. with the four walls 'folded down' from the sides of the plan. A high coved ceiling with rectangular central flat framed in egg and dart moulding. The ceiling cornice with a deep frieze decorated with alternating anthemion and bell-shaped flower motifs which recur in the doorcase entablatures. Chair rail and carved skirting board. Two-bay window elevation with oval mirror surrounded by elaborate plasterwork. Standard six-panel doors. (pl. 60).

Scale: $2\frac{7}{8}$ in. to 5 ft.

Insc. with dimensions and *Section in the Bed Chamber in the one pair of Stairs Story over Drawing Room at Mamhead* (see cat. 131 above); numbered *8*.

Pen and ink with grey washes 604 x 478

D. 2176–1896

Prov.: Rimell & Son.

This room is identified as Lady Lisburne's Dressing Room on the survey plan cat. 124 above.

134 Design for a dining room. Elevations of a rectangular room 22 ft. by 30 ft., and 13 ft. 3 in. high with the four walls 'folded down' from the sides of the plan. Rich but not elaborate. Ceiling cornice; deep frieze of alternating anthemion and inverted lotus, repeated in the entablature of the doorcases. Chair rail and carved skirting board. Three-bay window elevation with square reveals and enriched architraves. Square looking glasses between the windows. (pl. 61).

Scale: $2\frac{7}{8}$ in. to 5 ft.

Insc. with dimensions and *Section of the Dining Room at Mamhead*; numbered *14*.

Pen and ink with grey wash and water-colour 600x452

D. 2172–1896

Prov.: Rimell & Son.

This room corresponds to the dining room shown in plan (cat. 114) above.

135 Design for the plasterwork of a dining room ceiling. To match cat. 134 above. An elaborate and rather heavy design based on concentric ovals. The central oval, 5 ft. 6 in. is a painted scene of nine classical figures with musical instruments. This is surrounded by a Vitruvian scroll border, a broader border of wide flutes with scalloped ends, and a guilloche border with moulded edges. The main field of the ceiling is decorated with an oval ring of lightly intertwined circles of laurel leaves and then a heavy oval reeded moulding bound with fillets and rosettes. Naturalistic vine leaf garlands modelled to a large scale and hanging in deep loops are intertwined round the outermost moulding. Trophies of musical instruments hang from the garlands at either end and the corners of the ceiling are filled with baskets of flowers contained within the vine leaf loops. The baskets coloured naturalistically. The figure panel on a cobalt blue ground. (pl. 62).

Scale: $2\frac{7}{8}$ in. to 5 ft.

Insc. *Design of a Cieling*[sic] *for the Diningroom at Mamhead in Devonshire 30 by 22*.

Pen and ink with colour washes 467x626

D.2173–1896

Prov.: Rimell & Son.

136 Design for a Library. Elevation of a rectangular room. 21 ft. by 19 ft. 9 in. with the four walls 'folded down' from the sides of the plan. An elegant and fully developed library scheme with a symmetrical arrangement of bookcases accommodated as flat topped aedicules with Adam Ionic pilasters. The entablature has a diaper motif which is repeated in the frieze of the ceiling cornice. Acroterian statuettes are placed above the pilasters with shallow panels of classical reliefs set between. A more sculpturesque panel of three figures sacrificing at a house altar is set in a lugged frame above the chimneypiece. (pl. 63).

Scale: $2\frac{7}{8}$ in. to 5 ft.

Insc. with dimensions and *Section of the Library at Mamhead. The Seat of The Right Honble Lord Lisburne*.

Pen and ink with grey wash 520x640

D. 2174–1896

Prov.: Rimell & Son.

137 Design for a Library ceiling. To match cat. 136 above. A crisp and clearly structured circular pattern in an almost square field. The central acanthus boss, surrounded in a guilloche border is contained in an octagonal border of alternately straight and concave sides. From the points of this border lines of flower bell drops radiate to a wide fluted moulding (the strongest in the whole ceiling about 9 in. across) from which precise bay leaf garlands extend in a succession of loops round the whole design. Large flower rosettes fill the corners and the eight segments between the octagonal central border and the large fluted circle are filled alternately with arabesques of foliage, tendrils and urns, and with painted plaques of allegorical figures relating to different branches of knowledge. (pl. 64).

Scale: $2\frac{7}{8}$ in. to 5 ft.

Insc. *Design of a Cieling for the Library at Mamhead in Devonshire*; numbered *9*.

Pen and ink with colour washes and body colour 460x564

D. 2175–1896

Prov.: Rimell & Son.

The colour range proposed here is cool and sophisticated; pale mustard yellow, warm pink, *eau de nil* and terracotta with turquoise borders. Of all the proposals for individual rooms at Mamhead, this attractive scheme for a small, square library fits most closely with the survey plan (cat. 123) above and with two of the sets of plans (cat. 114, 117 above). It does not correspond exactly however as the Library planned for the north-east corner of the house is shown with the interior divided by pilasters on the plan and was to have had a door in the fireplace wall connecting to the hall in the north range. No door is shown here. The treatment of the bookshelves as classical aedicules is a standard Adam solution of Library design in the late 1760s and the 1770s. It may be noted also at Osterley (see cat. 84); at Mellerstain and at Nostell Priory.

Professor Damie Stillman has kindly provided me with copies of notes he made of building papers relating to Mamhead that belonged to Sir Ralph Newman Bt., whose family purchased the property in 1823. The whereabouts of these papers in not now known: from the notes it is however possible to date the plans and elevations in the museum's collection to 1766 when John Hobcroft, a local builder, submitted estimates for four separate contracts: (i) a reconstruction (of the old house), (ii) new staircases and watercloset, (iii) building and finishing the north side 'according to a plan given by Robert Adam Esqr architect' and (iv) building the south side of the house. The scheme must have remained a possibility for some time as copies of the ceiling designs in the Soane Museum (see cat. 132, 135 & 137 above) are dated 1769.

Designs (on 5 sheets) for alternative schemes for additions to Mamhead old house by John Johnson of Berners Street, Cavendish Square, London. c.1779.

138 Ground floor plan proposing the extension of the rooms to left and right of the hall, to convert the existing nine-bay front into eleven bays.

s. *J. Johnson Berners Street, Cavendish Square, London*;

Insc. *Design for Alteration of Mamhead* and with notes.

Pen and ink with yellow wash and pencil 337x523

D. 2192–1896

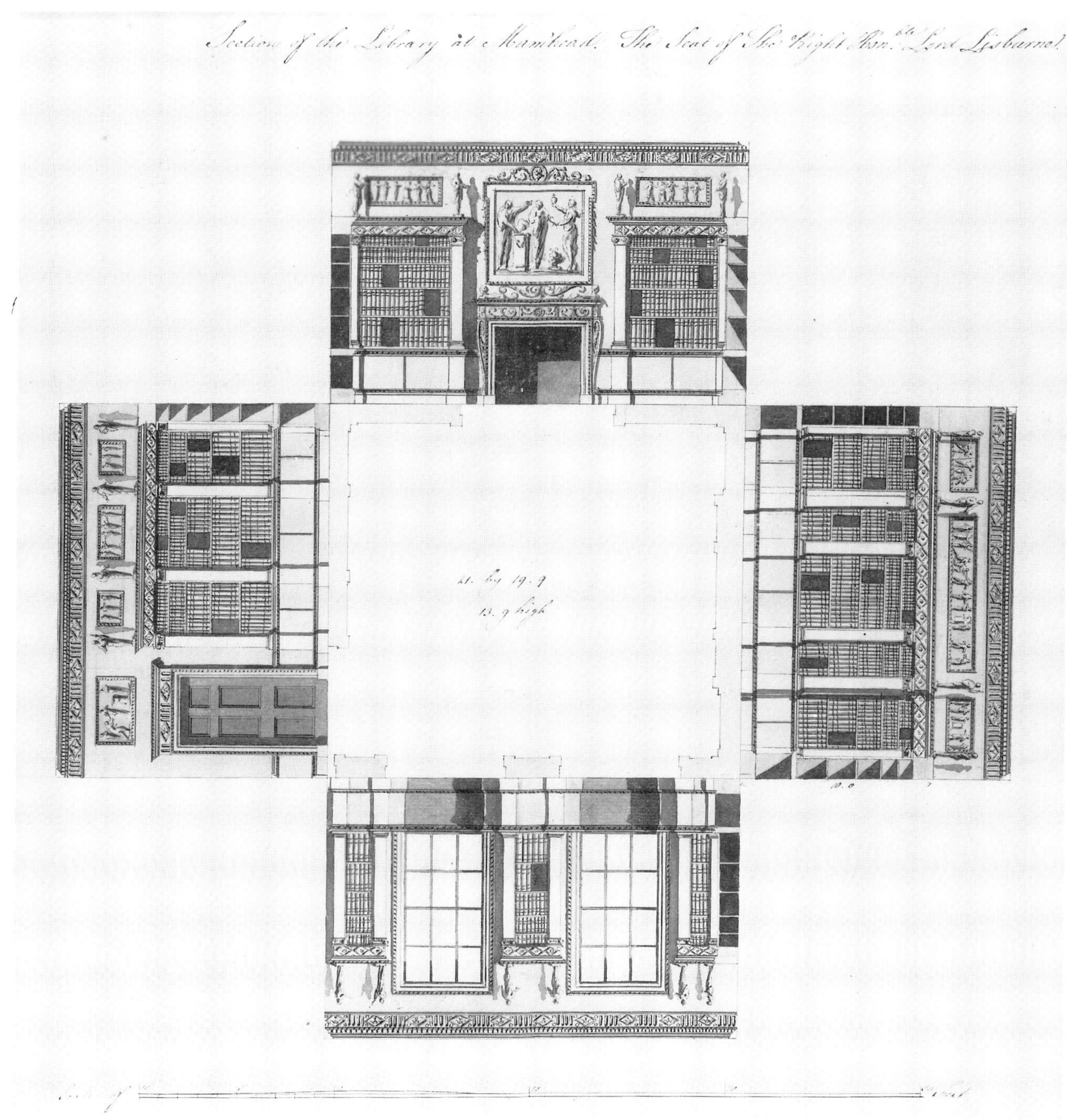

PLATE 63 (cat. 136)

139 Ground-floor plan of a larger scheme proposing a new north range with a bowed central projection and an eleven-bay entrance front.

Scale: $\frac{7}{8}$ in. to 10 ft.

s. *J. Johnson* and insc. *Berners Street*, *Cavendish Square* and *design for Addition to Mamhead* and with dimensions and notes.

Pen and ink and yellow wash 344 x 491

D. 2189–1896

140 First-floor plan of the larger scheme.

Scale: $\frac{7}{8}$ in. to 10 ft.

s. *J. Johnson* and insc. *Bed Room Story* and with dimensions and notes.

Pen and ink and yellow wash 354 x 500

D. 2190–1896

PLATE 64 (cat. 137)

141 Attic floor plan of the larger scheme.
Scale: $\frac{7}{8}$ in. to 10 ft.
s. *J. Johnson* and insc. with dimensions and notes and *Attic Story*.
Pen and ink with yellow wash 342 x 490
D. 2191–1896

142 Elevation of the new north front proposed in the larger scheme. A long seven-bay, three-storey front with a central three-bay bow. Quoin pilasters at the ends with urn finials, string courses and flat entablatures to the ground-floor and first-floor windows.
Scale: $\frac{7}{8}$ in. to 10 ft.
s. *J. Johnson*.
Pen and ink wash 285 x 462
D. 2188–1896

Johnson's designs for Mamhead are not dated though it is likely that they were commissioned about 1778 or 1779 when he designed Killerton Park near Exeter for Lord Lisburne's neighbour Sir Thomas Acland Bart. The previous year Johnson had been taken to court by the Adam brothers for infringing their patent to manufacture stucco. The case was tried by Lord Chief Justice Mansfield, a client and friend of the Adam brothers who in giving a judgement in their favour laid himself open to the charge of partiality. The affair became a *cause celèbre* in which a good deal of criticism was focused onto Robert and James Adam. Johnson was well connected in the city with building and banking interests and Lord Lisburne's approach to him in this peiod may reflect a general feeling that he had been unfairly treated and had suffered from sharp practice at the hands of the Adam brothers. If sentiments of this sort inspired Lord Lisburne's commission, Johnson was no more successful in bringing his patron to the point of building at Mamhead than Robert Adam had been.

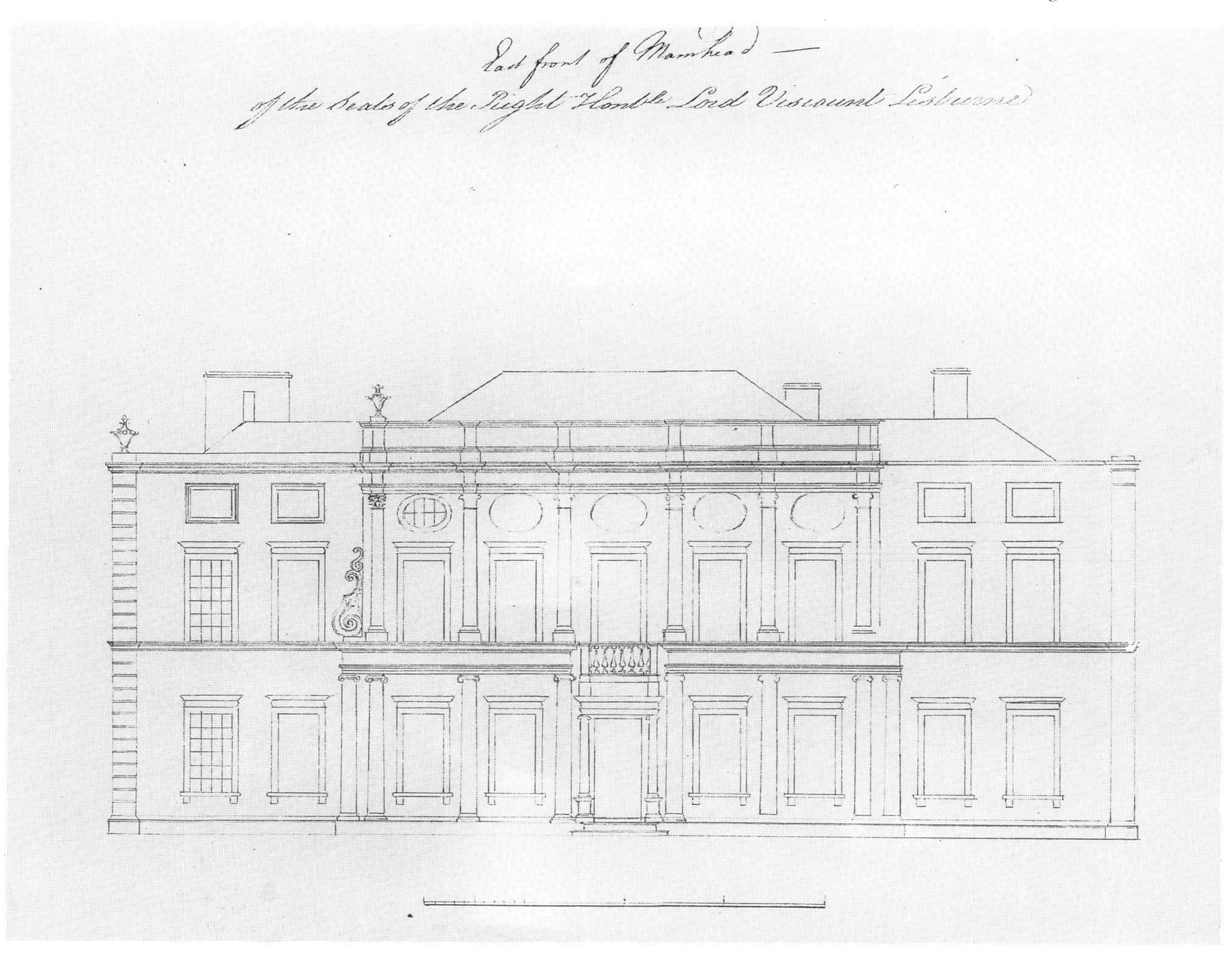

PLATE 65. Robert Adam. Mamhead House, record elevation of east front. (Sir John Soane's Museum.)

PLATE 66. Mamhead House. (Engraving by S. Lacey in J. P. Neale, Views of Seats, 1821.)

PLATE 67 (cat. 143)

PLATE 68 (cat. 144)

MISTLEY, Norfolk, Mistley Hall

Reservoir for a salt-water bath for the Rt. Hon. Richard Rigby M.P. 1774.

143 A perspectival sketch of a segmental basin of water backed by trees, foliage and an architectural facade. The facade derives ultimately from Italian sixteenth-century garden architecture: a deep arch with a reclining statue on a plinth is flanked by a pair of statue niches framed by heavy Doric columns with icicle rustication. (pl. 67).

Insc. by C. J. Richardson *R. Adam* and on *verso*, *Sketch of the reservoir for the Bath at Mistley for the Right Honble Richard Rigby – R Adam.*

Pen and ink 195x290

3436.21

Prov.: C. J. Richardson.

This design, which was not to be built, is recorded first as a roughly drawn pencil elevation in the Soane Museum and as a finished proposal in plan and elevation (S.M.D., Vol. I, No. 165 and Vol. 41, No. 59). The bath itself is shown Vol. 41, No. 53–58. Bolton discusses Adam's work at Mistley in Bolton 1922, Vol. 2, chap. 25.

TULLOCH CASTLE, Cromarty, Highland Region

Design for a ruined tower for Duncan Davidson 1790.

144 Freehand sketch plan of a round tower containing a wide spiral staircase, with a subsidiary round tower stump, a ruined wall with an arch and a third square tower stump. Pictorial elevation above. (pl. 68).

Insc. In Adam's hand *Paleing* and by Richardson *Adams.*

Pen and sepia ink with grey and brown wash, the sheet trimmed 160x234

3436.12

Prov.: C. J. Richardson.

Both in its draughtsmanship and architectural style this sketch of a folly tower is highly characteristic of the Adams' late Picturesque work. The paling linking the principal tower to the smaller round stump appears in numerous 'fancy' projects and was executed, in stone, at either end of Adam's bridge over the river Aln at Alnwick. The machicolated round tower is also a common motif appearing in such Adam castles as Dalquharran, Culzean and Pitfour, in several unbuilt projects and in the Picturesque drawings, see cat. 26 below.

This particular project dates from early in 1790. Adam proposed at least three schemes for castle-style ruins for Duncan Davidson: the largest of these is dated 9 May 1789; a smaller version is dated to 20 August the same year and the final project, which is the smallest and is based on this sketch, is inscribed 'Sketch of an old tower for Duncan Davidson Esqr near Cromarty, Albermarle Street 28 April 1790'. These drawings are S.M.D., Vol. 10, Nos 67 and 133 and Vol. 48, Nos. 103–106.

WYRESIDE, near Cockerham, Lancashire

Elevations (on 3 sheets) of two schemes for additions to a small eighteenth-century farm or manor house for John Fenton Cawthorn M.P. c.1790.

145 First design for a new entrance front for a small Classical villa. A pedimented two-storey block, one room in width with a projecting Doric porch of four columns and a group of three windows above. This is flanked by single-bay, single-storey wings and linked by low screen walls to square pavilions on each side with eaves pediments supporting a shallow lead dome. Pricked through.

Scale: 1½ in. to 10 ft.

Insc. in an office hand *For John Fenton Cawthorn Esq*, and at bottom left in pencil *R. Adam.*

Pencil and pen and ink with grey washes 233x500

3328

Prov.: C. J. Richardson.

An unidentified outline version of this design is among the Adam sketches volumes (S.M.D. Vol. I, No. 50 verso).

146 Second version of the new entrance front. Essentially the same design as cat. 145 above except that the single-bay wings flanking the central block are raised to two storeys, the screen walls are slightly more substantial and the terminal square pavilions are different. Here they have tri-partite windows set in a relieving arch (in place of a plain round-headed opening in an arch) and the pavilion domes rise from a flat coping stone without the complication of four pediments. Pricked through. (pl. 69).

Scale: 1½ in. to 10 ft.

Insc. In an office hand *West Front of a House for John Fenton Cawthorn Esquire* and at bottom left in pencil *R. Adam.*

Pencil, pen and ink with grey washes 266x498

3329

Prov.: C. J. Richardson.

An unidentified outline version of part of this design is among the Adam sketches volumes (S.M.D., Vol. I, No. 50).

147 Side elevation to accompany the second version of the new front. Two domed pavilions, as in cat. 146 above, flank a low square tower, three-storey by three bays, with a tri-partite central doorway set inside a large fan light and three circular windows to the top storey. The tower roof is pyramidal and ends in an Adam weather-vane. Pricked through.

Scale: 1½ in. to 10 ft.

Insc. In office hand *South front of a House for John Fenton Cawthorn Esqr.*

Pencil, pen and ink with grey washes 262x458

3330

Prov.: C. J. Richardson.

In many ways the Adam designs for Wyreside are typical of much of the brothers' practice towards the ends of their lives. Like several of their proposed villas in Scotland, the scale of Mr. Cawthorn's design was modest: the main block in the larger scheme was only 54 ft. wide. Yet this small house is treated in a manner that is architecturally highly self-conscious, employing a number of different ideas each of which is typical of the late Adam style. The bowl shaped domes as terminal features, the four columned Tuscan porch, the tripartite aediculed window and the central tower motif of the south front had, by the date of this scheme, all become standard elements in the Adam villa repertoire. The brothers however thought sufficiently well of the second version of the scheme to have prepared copy drawings of it (S.M.D. Vol. 46, No. 109 and 110) for inclusion in an intended publication of their later work (see Rowan 1985, pl. 30). These drawings for the book exhibit an odd plan that bears little real relation to either elevation and is tacked on to an earlier house in a haphazard way. Adam also prepared a castle style scheme (S.M.D. Vol. 36, No. 99 and 100) and it was apparently a hybrid version of this Classical villa retaining the other gothic wings that was begun about 1790 (pl. 70). By this date the screen walls had become two-storey links and may always have been built as such. In 1836 Wyreside was purchased by Robert Garrett and soon afterwards refaced as a continuous two-storey Classical facade whose major subdivisions nonetheless bear a generic similarity to Adam's Classical scheme.

Unidentified Designs

Architecture

DESIGN FOR AN IRON STAIR RAIL

148 Detailed design (or possibly working drawing) for a wrought-iron banister and hand-rail. Four banisters are shown: two on a landing and two on the slope of a stair. The design is an elongated fluted and tapered plinth – like the lower part of a herm – with a rectangular block top with rams' heads at the corners below it. This supports a plinth decorated with an anthemion and then a vase just below the rail. Husk garlands hang from the rams' heads and link each banister.

Scale: 3 in. to 1 ft.

Pen and ink with grey wash 376x295

3331

Prov.: C. J. Richardson.

A. T. Bolton has noted on this drawing 'Probably Osterley Park, Nostell or Home House'. Clearly an Adam design the drawing does not match exactly with any of the stairs suggested by Bolton. It is closest to the balustrade to the outside garden staircase at Osterley though this lacks the rectangular section above the rams' heads and replaces the urn at the top with an open box. It may be noted however that the rather short treads shown here – only 10 in. while those at Harewood are 1 ft. 2 in. (cf. cat. 60) – would accord well with the curved profile and wedge-shaped steps on the Osterley stair. Adam used parallel bars for a balustrade surmounted by an urn at Culzean Castle and at Wormleybury either of which might have been developed out of this design. The scale of this drawing at quarter full-size is standard for the Adam office.

DESIGN FOR A FRIEZE AND CORNICE FOR A ROOM

149 Large-scale outline elevation with sections of the mouldings on the left. Plasterer's drawing probably half full-size. A dentil cornice and guilloche architrave (partly incomplete) with a frieze of foliage tendril spirals which end alternately in a pair of putti (only one shown) pouring water into a dish, and a house altar with ram's head corners and sphinx base.

Insc. in ink $\frac{5}{8}$' on one moulding and in pencil by Richardson *Adams*.

Pen and ink and wash 207x464

3436.61

Prov.: C. J. Richardson.

DESIGNS FOR COLUMNAR SCREENS

Adamesque designs (on 3 sheets) for columnar screens in a dining room with recesses for side-boards.

150 Part plan and elevation of a rectangular recess for a room that is 15 ft. wide with square Doric pilasters and a detached column framing the recess. Alternative frieze, capitals and column shafts shown and an Adamesque rectangular side-board.

Scale: $\frac{1}{2}$ in. to 1 ft.

Pen and ink and wash 235x286

D. 1251–1898

Prov.: E. Parsons, 1898.

PLATE 69 (cat. 146)

PLATE 70 Wyreside, entrance front. (Etching and aquatint from *the Lonsdale Magazine*, 1821.)

151 Part plan and elevation of a columnar screen across the end of a room that is 17 ft. wide. The corners of the room are canted with doors on each side screened by an invented Adam Order of columns with a low segmental arch spanning the central space. A bow-fronted Adamesque side-board with winecooler below.

Scale: ½ in. to 1 ft.

Pen and ink and wash 342x275

D. 1252–1898

Prov.: E. Parsons, 1898.

152 Part plan and elevation of a columnar screen across a segmental apse at the end of a large room. Pilaster responds and detached columns of a fluted invented Order frame the recess which contains a low-fronted Adamesque side-board with Neo-classical urns, plates and knife boxes.

Pen and ink with colour washes 312x240

D. 1253–1898

Prov.: E. Parsons, 1898.

DESIGN FOR AN ASSEMBLY ROOM

153 Plan of a large rectangular room – a double square – the four walls 'folded down' to show the interior decoration. The short end elevations have three plain windows on two storeys with rosettes and floral drops between. The long walls have symmetrical door cases at either end with a central fireplace facing a tall arched recess with a balcony presumably for a band. Room cornice of alternating bows and floral swags, with clumsy geometrical panels on the walls. The walls light green. c.1775.

Pen and ink with washes 374x509

D. 1839–1885

Prov.: E. Parsons, 1885.

This anonymous design, characteristic of many a provincial interior in the last quarter of the eighteenth century, well illustrates the effect on minor designers of the Adam brothers' manner and the extent to which their style was to become common property in late Georgian Britain.

Chimneypiece designs

Of the designs by Adam listed below, two represent finished proposals for chimneypieces of a distinctly sculptural character, another is a rapid sketch of a similarly sculptural scheme and one is a line drawing of Palladian character. The remainder (on 5 sheets) are slight sketches of half designs. These are the only unidentified designs for chimneypieces which on account of their provenance, draughtsmanship or style may be accepted as Adam's work. There is also in the Museum's collection a number of anonymous eighteenth-century drawings for chimneypieces (cat. 163–189), which reflect, in varying degrees, the dissemination of the Adam style. Several which were acquired in the late nineteenth century have forged signatures or else an address linking them with the brothers' practice. Clearly these have no real connection with the Adam office yet their authenticity as historical designs and their stylistic affinity with the brothers' style – a style that was spread rapidly if in a watered-down way through the building manuals – may justify their inclusion here as the work of Adamesque designers. Also included are two designs with fake Adam inscriptions now known to be the work of Henry Holland.

154 Sketch elevation of a sculptural caryatid chimneypiece. Two large scale, free standing female figures flank the fireplace opening and hold back a heavy drapery to reveal a tall sculpted panel above the centre with a tripod of three nude figures supporting a clock set above it. A continuous cornice over the plaque and above the heads of the main figures is lightly indicated. (pl. 71).

Insc. In C. J. Richardson's hand *R Adams figures by Cipriani.*

Pen and ink with grey wash over pencil 170x165

3436.46

Prov.: C. J. Richardson.

The popularity of caryatid chimneypieces such as Adam proposes here may be traced back to the example of Isaac Ware's design for the chimneypiece of the Great Drawing Room in Chesterfield House, London of c.1748. This is published as plate 88 in Ware's *Complete Body of Architecture* of 1756 while the chimneypiece itself is now in the Metropolitan Museum, New York (see Parker 1963). The Adam family in Edinburgh found Ware's book a useful source for its own work and Lord Chesterfield's design lies behind the sculptured chimneypiece executed by Rysbrack to John and Robert Adam's specification for the Earl of Hopetoun in 1756. Robert later used essentially the same idea for Admiral Boscawen at Hatchlands in 1759 and again in June 1777 in his third design for the gallery chimneypiece at Harewood, the finished drawing for which is now in the Metropolitan Museum, New York (34,78.2.(7)) see pl. 72. The design recorded here is apparently an alternative proposal for Harewood. Its left-hand figure though more robustly employed with her draperies, is identical in pose to that of the New York drawing and also to the same figure, in what is presumably another preparatory sketch in the Soane Museum, where a pediment replaces the tripod and clock (S.M.D., Vol. 22, No. 18).

PLATE 71 (cat. 154)

A more elaborate caryatid chimneypiece alternative, unassociated with any specific commission (S.M.D., Vol. 24, No. 192) proposed Indian and African (?) figures with arms, as here, outstretched across the fire place opening. It seems reasonable to accept Richardson's suggestion that a hand other than Adam's drew these figures. A note on one of the drawings for Harewood in the Soane Museum suggests that Nollekens was to have been the sculptor of this design.

155 Freehand sketch elevation of an elaborately sculptural chimneypiece, flanked by male herms. The herm (only the left-hand stile is shown) is canted at 45 degrees to the line of the wall and raises its right arm to support a salient entablature with reclining lions above. The centre of the transom has a relief panel of three figures set as a block in the frieze with a salient cornice above supporting a deep cavetto moulding with a tall urn. Swags of foliage drop from the handles of the urn to the lions' tales. Alternatives for the panel and urn are lightly sketched above and below the main design. For the *recto* of this sheet see cat. 13.

s. in pencil *R. Adam.*

Pen and sepia ink with grey wash 197x205

3436.47 (*verso*)

Prov.: C. J. Richardson.

PLATE 72 Robert Adam. Elevation of the chimneypiece for the Gallery at Harewood house, Yorkshire. Pen and ink and water-colour. (The Metropolitan Museum of Art, Harris Brisbane Dick Fund, 1934.)

This bold sketch probably dates from Adam's Roman period: a view on the other side of the sheet is of the *Trinità dei Monti* and the almost obsessive use of sculptural forms must reflect an early response by the young architect to contact with Roman antiquities. The positioning of the herm, canted at an angle, also seems to relate to work early in Adam's career. Though the effect of this sketch is clumsy the design has a certain *brio* and the drawing is perhaps more like one done with a bad pen than by a bad draughtsman!

156 Finished elevation of a chimneypiece with half-size figures of Apollo and Diana, a central plaque representing a presentation to Diana and various trophies of the hunt: horns, quivers of arrows, fox heads and chained hounds. (pl. 73).

Pencil, pen and ink and grey wash with water-colour 227x299

8897.14

Prov.: E. Parsons, 1882.

The light-hearted fancy reflected in this design, which must surely relate to a hunting lodge or a commission for the rooms of a particular hunt, is characteristic of Adam's approach. Frequently his designs for library chimney pieces introduce terrestial and celestial globes or armillary spheres as appropriate emblems for a study, while for individual patrons heraldic supporters or elements from a family crest may be similarly incorporated. The soft style of the draughtsmanship, paricularly in the figures and the panel scene, would seem to indicate Adam's hand while the right-angled shadow cast in the opening of the hearth is consistent both with Adam's office practice and with the published work of G. B. Piranesi from whom the brothers may well have copied this particular form of presentation.

The style of the chimneypiece itself may also owe a debt to Piranesi or to Italian rather than to English examples. For a native design the use of half-length sculpted figures on the styles is unusual: full scale caryatids or herms (see cat. 154 and 155 above), or columns are normal in this position yet in Piranesi's *Diverse maniere d'adornare i cammini* of 1769 a number of designs are published using high relief half length figures such as Adam proposes here. John Bacon copied one of these (pl. 38) for the Drawingroom chimneypiece at Burton Constable, Yorkshire about 1775 (see Hall 1982) while the Adam brothers introduced similar figures in the chimneypiece of the Second Drawing room at Derby House designed in 1773 (Adam 1773, Vol. II, No. 1, pl. III) and again in the chimney piece of the First Drawing room of Sir Watkin Williams Wynn's house in 1778 (S.M.D. Vol. 23, No. 10). A second oddity of the design is provided by the bases of the statues: no plan is given but the shading and the shadows which they cast clearly suggest two, three-dimensional, half round plinths projecting into the room and this unusual motif recurs in a set of anonymous Italian designs for chimney pieces now in the Pierpont Morgan Library in New

PLATE 73 (cat. 156)

PLATE 74 Chimneypiece in the Oriental Club, London (see cat. 156).

York (1958, 23;6, 7 and 8; see Stillman 1977). It appears too in a chimneypiece of exceptional quality now in the Library of the Oriental Club, Stratford Place (pl. 74). This chimneypiece was installed in the building in the late nineteenth century by the Earl of Derby, the descendant of one of Adam's most noted patrons. Its origin is not documented yet it has interesting parallels with the Adam design recorded here. It reproduces again the idea of two half length statues on the styles of the hearth; they stand on curved drum bases that project slightly from the bases that contain them; and the transom above the fireplace is decorated with four roundels of allegorical figures of astronomy, sculpture, painting and architecture very much in the tradition of Robert Adam's decorative inventions.

157 Finished outline drawing of carved chimneypiece. Unorthodox console brackets, and foliage bell drops decorate the stiles which break forward as a salient cornice at the transom level. Centre plaque of a lion with its foot on a ball.

Pen and ink 111x187

3436.335

Prov.: C. J. Richardson.

While this traditionally Kentian chimneypiece is not immediately typical of the Adam style a design of a similar character and hand exists in the Soane Museum (S.M.D. vol. 23 f.193). The crisp bead and fillet in the architrave and more especially the foliage bell drops may be paralleled in numerous Adam designs (see cat. 87, 90, 94, 98–100).

158 Finished elevation of a chimneypiece with large console brackets to the stiles, the transom decorated with an urn flanked by griffons whose tails develop into acanthus tendril decoration. c.1760.

Scale: 1½ in to 16ft.

Pen and ink with water-colour 305x492

E. 2115–1913

Prov.: purchased, 1913.

The style of this chimneypiece is characteristic of Adam's manner in the early country-house commissions after his return from Italy when a certain residual Palladian robustness is fused with more recently learnt antique detail such as decorates the transom in this design.

159 Sketch of the left half of an Etruscan chimneypiece. A wide stile is decorated with a pair of slender Ionic pilasters flanking arabesque decoration that rises from an urn. The cornice has a shallow blocking course with scrolled plinth above the pilasters and the centre of the transom is marked by a projecting sculpted tablet.

Insc. In Richardson's hand *by Robert Adam.*

Pencil 167x148

3436.36

Prov.: C. J. Richardson.

This light pencil sketch of elaborately delicate design is typical both of Adam's style of drawing in the 1770s and of the methods of composition which he used when devising schemes of decoration for the town houses of his most wealthy clients. It may represent a first version of the design for the great drawing room for Sir John Hussey Delaval Bt. at Hanover Square of 1780. Its style is paralleled by other drawings in the Soane Museum (S.M.D. vol. 23, Nos. 185 & 189).

160 Rough sketches of the left-hand stiles and transoms of three chimneypieces with pencil details of a separate capital and a rapidly noted plan of a domed building.

Insc. in pencil in Richardson's hand *Adams.*

Pen and sepia ink with pencil alterations 158x104

3436.56

Prov.: C. J. Richardson.

These scratchy and rather curious designs presumably date from early in Adam's Roman period.

161 Sketches of a chimneypiece incorporating a pilaster, Diocletian or Lotus type capital and centre tablet with beaded surround. For the *recto* of this sheet see cat. 37.

Insc. with various measurements, eg. *3¾/6½/1.11½.*

Pencil 162x110

3436.23 (*verso*)

Prov.: C. J. Richardson.

This drawing though slight and sketchy is quite particular in its details and seems to be a note, by Adam, of a chimney piece whose unorthodox character caught his attention. The precise notes of dimensions would bear this out.

162 Rough sketch of the left-hand stile and half transom for a chimneypiece with a neo-medieval herm wearing a visor and suit of armour. Proportions altered to allow the base of the herm to be extended.

Insc. in Richardson's hand, *Adams* twice.

Pencil 167x120

3436.55

Prov.: C. J. Richardson.

This sketch is by Robert Adam.

Adamesque Chimneypiece Designs

163 Six elevations (only partially completed) for plain fire place surrounds with decorative Adamesque friezes above.

Insc. in pencil *West Parlor* and *Middle Room.*

Pencil and pen and ink 395x635

E. 602–1918

Prov.: given by Aleck Abrahams, 1918.

This sheet of straight-forward designs records the basic eighteenth-century fire place where the opening for the hearth is framed by three blocks of stone which are set within a projecting convex cornice. This simple form appears on the right-hand side of five of these designs. A first elaboration of the basic opening was to add a frieze and cornice across the top which might then be given extra decoration by a central panel, separately treated, or further enriched by the addition of stiles or pilasters down the sides of the hearth opening. Four of the designs have decorated friezes of an Adamesque or neo-classical character. The diamond pattern here intended for the 'Middle room' is one that recurs frequently in minor rooms in Adam's commissions. (See S.M.D. vol. 22, Nos. 85, 86, 97, 266; vol. 23, No. 29; vol. 24, Nos. 30 and 45).

164 Elevations of two Adamesque fire place surrounds with decorated friezes and narrow stiles.
Insc. *Dining Room Mr Powell* and *Front Parlor Mr Powell.*
Pen and ink and wash 210x366
E. 603–1918
Prov.: given by Aleck Abrahams, 1918.
These designs probably date from the third quarter of the eighteenth century.

165 Sketch elevation of an Adamesque chimneypiece of coloured marbles with many sculptural panels. The stiles decorated with a vertical panel of relief sculpture incorporating dishes, urns, floral elements and finial statuettes. The blocks of the frieze above have cameo portrait heads and the transom is decorated by a central plaque showing the young Bacchus in an oval flanked by further sculptural scenes. Parts of the design are incomplete. c.1780.
Pencil, pen and ink and water-colour 205x280
E. 967–1965
Prov.: Bequeathed by Rupert Gunnis.
This design, very much a vehicle for sculpture, has been attributed to Joseph Wilton. Its curious half round vases (see also cat. 156) certainly suggest a continental influence which would be possible with Wilton, or with Francis Harwood who executed many chimneypieces of exactly this character for English patrons in Florence in the 1760s and the 1770s. See Fleming and Honour 1968 and Rowan 1974 III.

166 Adamesque chimneypiece with a frieze of alternating groups of flutes and diamonds.
Forged inscription (see note below).
Pen and ink and wash 343x510
D. 305–1890
Prov.: E. Parsons.

167 Adamesque chimneypiece with a frieze of alternating anthemia and palmettes.
Forged inscription (see note below).
Pen and ink and wash 345x509
D. 308–1890
Prov.: E. Parsons.

168 Adamesque chimneypiece with a frieze decorated with paired satyrs leaning against a vase and foliage tendrils.
Forged inscription (see note below).
Pen and ink and wash 353x510
D. 309–1890
Prov.: E. Parsons.

169 Adamesque chimneypiece with a frieze decorated with tendrils. The stiles with half paterae and husk ropes.
Forged inscription (see note below).
Pen and ink and wash 350x510
D. 304–1890
Prov.: E. Parsons.

170 Adamesque chimneypiece with a frieze decorated with a lamp motif and tendrils. The stiles fluted and interrupted by a block near the top.
Forged inscription (see note below).
Pen and ink and coloured washes 340x506
D. 310–1890
Prov.: E. Parsons.

171 Adamesque chimneypiece with a fluted frieze. The styles with tapering shafts, beaded and moulded.
Forged inscription (see note below).
Pen and ink and grey wash 361x532
D. 319–1890
Prov.: E. Parsons.

172 Adamesque chimneypiece with centre tablet of a female figure and putto. Alternative treatment of frieze shown. The stiles with tapering shafts with flower bell garlands.
Forged inscription (see note below).
Pen and ink and grey wash 348x497
D. 317–1890
Prov.: E. Parsons.

173 Adamesque chimneypiece with a large central urn and frieze with swags. The stiles fluted, with tapering shafts and tripods at the top.
Forged inscription (see note below).
Pencil, pen and ink and grey wash 348x515
D. 315–1890
Prov.: E. Parsons.

174 Adamesque chimneypiece with a frieze decorated with flower bell garlands, central patera and foliage tendrils. The stiles show the side elevation of console brackets reversed.
Forged inscription (see note below).
Pen and ink and dark wash 349x510
D. 306–1890
Prov.: E. Parsons.

175 Adamesque chimneypiece with a frieze decorated with an oval panel of a female figure and an urn. Foliage tendrils and sphinxes either side. The stiles are console brackets upside down with Ionic capitals. Side elevation shows console profile.
Forged inscription (see note below).
Pen and ink and colour washes 355x514
D. 316–1890
Prov.: E. Parsons.

176 Adamesque chimneypiece with an elaborate architectural transom: an arabesque plaque flanked on its upper sides by a frieze of diamonds and anthemia. The stiles as regular and large console brackets.
Forged inscription (see note below).
Pen and ink and grey wash 351x511
D. 318–1890
Prov.: E. Parsons

177 Adamesque chimneypiece with a frieze decorated with a central arabesque tablet, flanked by drapery swags. The stiles, a vertical panel with grotesque decorative drops and beyond a half Ionic pilaster.
Forged inscription (see note below).
Pen and ink and grey washes 360x520
D. 313–1890
Prov.: E. Parsons.

178 Adamesque chimneypiece with a pulvinated, fluted frieze and central panel of bow, arrows and a laurel wreath. The architrave inset with a crenellated pattern in deep blue. The stiles are male herms seen side on. (pl. 75).
Forged inscription (see note below).
Pen and ink and grey wash with water-colour 337x485
D. 303–1890
Prov.: E. Parsons.

179 Adamesque chimneypiece with Ionic pilasters decorated with arabesques. The frieze with a central urn and paterae in laurel wreaths.
Forged inscription (see note below).
Pen and ink and grey wash with water-colour 354x512
D. 311–1890
Prov.: E. Parsons.

180 Adamesque chimneypiece with Ionic pilasters decorated with trophy drops. The frieze with a central urn and sphinxes flanked by alternating paterae and candelabra between deep flower bell wreaths. Side elevation also shown.
Forged inscription (see note below).
Pen and ink and grey wash 352x512
D. 300–1890
Prov.: E. Parsons.

181 Large Adamesque architectural chimneypiece with caryatid type female herms and a central sculptural panel depicting a scene of antique judgement or magnaminity.
Forged inscription (see note below).
Pen and ink and grey wash with water-colour 360x528
D. 312–1890
Prov.: E. Parsons.

The Museum's Register of Drawings records the acquisition of these designs for chimneypieces (with five others listed below) as 'chimney pieces by Robert Adam. Twenty one drawings dated 1775–80. Pr £15:0:0'. Each drawing bears two fake inscriptions in a nineteenth-century hand: the signature *R. Adam* and *Adelphi* together with a date ranging from 1775 to 1780. One (cat. 72) is also inscribed with a spurious note *Chimney piece for the Drawing Room*. The Museum's original numbering (D. 229 to D. 319–1890) arranged the designs chronologically according to the forged dates. Here they have been reordered according to their complexity beginning with the more simple designs. The drawings probably date from the late 1790s or the early 1800s. They clearly form a group and may possibly have been prepared by a young architect for publication or else, though this seems less likely, they may represent a set of designs prepared in the trade for a monumental mason to show to clients. That they are a set is proved by the number of features which they have in common. The shape and size of the sheets are very similar. All sixteen designs are drawn to the same scale of 1½ inches to a foot and, with the exception of cat. 173 which is unfinished, are framed by a single black border of about ⅛ inch thick. In all the draughtsmanship and presentation is comparable: the drawing is delicate but weak and comparatively inexperienced in the free hand passages; the washes are well handled – such as a competent student might apply – and all the projecting elements cast crisp shadows to set off the overall design.

With this young artist the brothers' doctrine that genius knows no fetters has at times been counter productive: the more elaborate designs are often too fussy (cat. 178 and 180) and the free treatment of console brackets is very odd (cat. 183 and 184 below). While many of the individual motifs were certainly popularised by the Adam brothers the use of husk ropes (cat. 170 and 180) is more characteristic of Sir William Chambers and his pupils or of influences from France. For Mr Parsons see p. 24 above.

182 Architectural Adamesque chimneypiece with female caryatid type herms. A fluted pulvinated frieze with a central sculpted panel of cupid in a chariot drawn by a bear and a goat.
Insc. and d. falsely by *Adelphi 1775*.
Pencil, pen and ink and wash 241x333
D.299–1890
Prov.: E. Parsons.

183 Adamesque chimneypiece with a frieze decorated with paterae in bay leaf wreaths. The stiles as console brackets with narrow necking shafts above.
Pen and ink and wash 323x483
D. 307–1890
Prov.: E. Parsons.

184 Sketch design for an Adamesque chimneypiece with a transom decorated by a blank oval plaque linked, by swags of fruit and flowers, to composite capitals set directly on top of console bracket stiles. Side elevation and sketch of alternative capital also shown.
Pen and ink and wash on grey paper 326x510
D. 301–1890
Prov.: E. Parsons.

These three designs are part of the collection bought from Mr Parsons in July 1890 as original Adam designs (see cat. 166–181 above). Though different in various ways – size, paper, scale or finish – from the sixteen designs listed as a group above, the artist would appear to be the same 'black border' designer.

185 Adamesque chimneypiece with a frieze of alternating anthemion and foliage motifs within an oval leaf shape. The styles treated as the side elevation of an attenuated console bracket.
Scale: 1¼ in. to 1 ft.
Pen and ink with grey washes and water-colour 191x262
D. 277–1894
Prov.: G. Lanser.

PLATE 75 (cat. 178)

186 Adamesque chimneypiece with a frieze of alternating groups of flutes and bell drop garlands, or foliage tendrils. The stiles with composed Ionic type capitals on shafts tapering to a torch-like base.

Pen and ink with grey washes and water-colour 195 x 252

D. 278–1894

Prov.: G. Lanser.

187 Adamesque chimneypiece with a central plaque of a roundel showing female figure beside an urn set in garlands. The stiles decorated with rams' skulls with garland drops. Veined yellow and brown marble inner frame.

Pen and ink with grey washes and water-colour 186 x 256

D. 275–1894

Prov.: G. Lanser.

188 Adamesque chimneypiece with a centre plaque of an urn flanked by two winged putti who sprout from plant tendrils. The stiles decorated with sphinx heads with grotesque drops. The inner frame inlaid with intertwined bay leaf garlands.

Pen and ink with grey washes and water-colour 198 x 243

D. 276–1894

Prov.: G. Lanser.

This attractive set of highly finished chimneypiece designs (cat. 185–188) 'ascribed to R. Adam' was purchased by the Museum from Mr Lanser in July 1894. They are not by Adam, nor apparently by an Adam office assistant, as the style of draughtmanship and presentation has none of the characteristics associated with the Adam firm. They are nonetheless highly competent designs, conventional in their main elements, yet making an intelligent use of crisp, neo-classical detail to achieve a rich effect.

189 Finished elevation of a simple chimneypiece design. Divided in two to show narrow fluted stiles filled with yellow marble on the left, open on the right. The frieze decorated with similar yellow marble fluting on the left, and with swags of small circles on the right. c.1790.

Pencil and water-colour 241 x 283

E. 968–1965

Prov.: Bequeathed by Rupert Gunnis.

190 Finished elevation of a marble chimneypiece with fluted frieze and a central plaque of an urn with griffon heads and garlands. The styles tapered fluted pilasters with crossed quivers and torches on the frieze block. White and mottled marble.

Scale: $\frac{3}{4}$ in. to 1 ft.

Insc. on *verso To Chas. A[?]mcotts Esq. M.P./at Kettlethorpe/near Newton/Lincolnshire.*

Pen and ink and water-colour 190 x 220

80

Prov.: acquired in 1857.

191 Side, front elevation and plan of a chimneypiece in the French style with semi-circular, tapered and spirally fluted 'table-leg' stiles and a shallow transom decorated with a single guilloche.

Insc. with fake signature *R. Adam Adelphi 1776* and in a late eighteenth-century hand *John Drummond Esq chimney piece for the great drawing room statuary.*

Pen and ink and grey wash with coloured washes 318 x 466

D. 302–1890

Prov.: E. Parsons.

192 Side, front elevation, and plan of a chimneypiece in the French style. The sides, a quarter circle curved and fluted, partly contain two metal dishes supported on paw feet and an elongated central shaft. The transom is a shallow frieze of flower garlands.

Insc. with fake signature *R. Adam Adelphi 1780* and *Downing Street chimney piece* (piece written over an erased inscription).

Pen and ink and wash 288 x 438

D. 314–1890

Prov.: E. Parsons.

These two chimneypiece designs are part of the collection bought from Mr Parsons in July 1890 as original Adam designs (see cat. 181 above). The signatures are forgeries and the drawings are in reality by Henry Holland of whose style and draughtsmanship they are quite characteristic. John Drummond, a member of the eighteenth-century banking firm, rebuilt his house at 14 Spring Gardens, after a fire in 1795 and it is possible that the chimneypiece for the 'great drawing room' relates to this rebuilding (see *Survey of London*, Vol. XX, 1940). The drawing here given as for Downing Street is closely similar to chimneypieces designed by Holland for Woburn Abbey and for the Library at Southill. For these see Dorothy Stroud 1966, pls. 106 and 108.

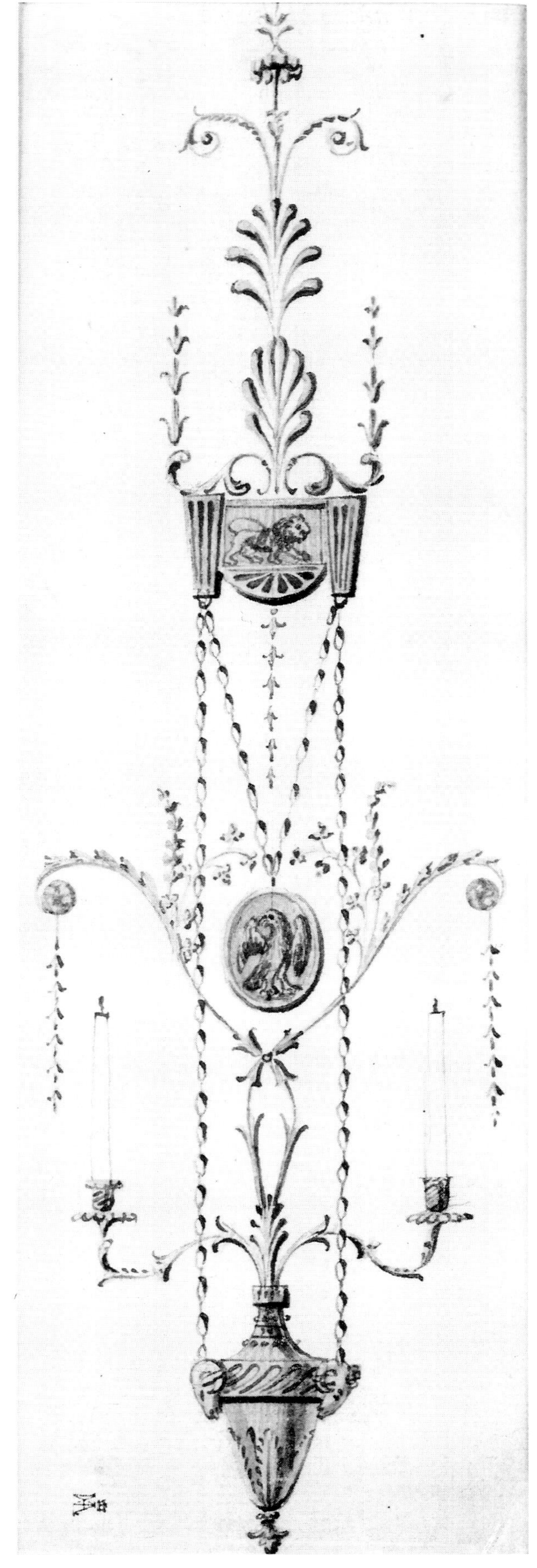

PLATE 76 (cat. 194)

Furniture and metalwork

193 Design for a silver candlestick. Full size sketch elevation in the form of a baluster, with anthemion decorations to the base and a spirally fluted upper shaft. 1 ft. 3 in. tall and 6 in. diameter. *verso* further pencil sketch for a candlestick.

Insc. in Richardson's hand *R. Adam.*

Pencil with part section and alterations in pen and sepia ink. Irregular, made up to 390x145

3436.48

Prov.: C. J. Richardson.

This confident drawing is characteristic of many Adam sketch designs of details and is a study for a finished candlestick design in the Soane Museum, S.M.D. Vol. 25, No. 97. Though this drawing is not inscribed with a client's name candlesticks of the type, with a square base matching the square top, were made by John Carter in 1767 (see Rowe 1967, pl. 10). Balusters used to support the nozzle of a candlestick appear in a design for Sir John Griffin, Bt., and in another anonymous design (S.M.D. Vol. 6, Nos. 3 and 70).

194 Design for a girandole. Freehand elevation of intricate design. A double sconce, which sprouts from an urn with rams' heads, hangs on gilded chains from a plaque high above it, with a medallion of an eagle and foliage tendril arabesques between. The plaque is decorated with a lion and has anthemion motifs above it. (pl. 76).

Pen and sepia ink with water-colour 246x62

D. 357–1885

Prov.: Bought from Mr E. Parsons, 23 Feb 1885.

The gilded chains in this design introduce a motif that does not occur in Adam's documented work. The character of the design is otherwise eminently Adamesque and it may be assumed to have been produced by a designer, if not in the Adams' employment, then closely associated with them.

195 Design for a tripod torchere. Finished elevation of a circular, gilt tripod supporting a metal-mounted porcelain or white marble vase with elaborate tendril scrolled sconces. Goats' head finials with crossed curling horns are set at the top of each leg of the tripod with husk-rope loops hanging from them and dropping down to an urn at its base. (pl. 77).

Pen and ink, with grey wash and water-colour 288x115

8168

Prov.: Bought from Mr R. Jackson, 1877.

Though evidently a design of about the last quarter of the eighteenth century the details and the drawing of this torchere place it outside the Adam *œuvre*. The goats' heads, husk ropes and hard channelled edges to the tripod legs are all untypical of the Adams' designs while the ambiguities of the draughtsmanship almost suggest an amateur. Is this a triangular or a circular torchere? And how will the candle brackets appear from another angle?

PLATE 77 (cat. 195)

196 Sketch design for a candlestick. Student's design on paw feet with the sketch of an alternative version.

Insc. *AA/BB/CC.*

Pencil, pen and ink with water-colour 232 x 106

8158.4

Prov.: Bought from Mr E. Parsons, 29 May 1877.

This amusingly awkward design (with paw feet on paw feet) seems to record a student muddle the key to which is given by the light pencil version of the candlestick drawn beside it and by the letters A, B and C all *upside down.* What seems to have happened is that a junior draughtsman was asked to enlarge a sketch of a baluster candlestick but got the ends muddled up!

197 Design for a commode. Three-bay front with inset cameos. A rough sketch with drawing of an urn below.

Insc. *Design of a commode for the 2nd Drawing room at Aspley House* and at bottom left *Robt Adam/Adelphi Oct 10th 1777.*

Pencil, pen and ink 250 x 275

E. 3225–1938

Prov.: bought from G. Heywood Hill, 1938.

This drawing of a piece of Adam furniture, together with one in the collection of the Cooper-Hewitt Museum, New York, is a forgery. No authentic drawings by the Adam brothers, or their office, are drawn on this type of soft tinted paper. The source of the design, which is incompetently copied is an Adam drawing (S.M.D. Vol. 17, No. 43), reproduced in Bolton 1922, Vol. II, Chapter XX where he discusses Adam's furniture designs. This connection was recognised at the time of acquisition. The Cooper-Hewitt drawing is a compound forgery using three further illustrations from the same chapter in Bolton's book.

Select Bibliography

All published in London unless otherwise mentioned.

Published Work by the Adam Brothers

Robert Adam, *Ruins of the Palace of the Emperor Diocletian at Spalatro*, 1764.

Robert and James Adam, *The Works in Architecture of Robert and James Adam*, 3 volumes, 1773, 1779 and 1822.

The *Works in Architecture* were issued in parts from 1773 but did not proceed in the regular manner the brothers had at first intended. The didactic preface and first part of the first volume are all that date from 1773; the frontispiece dates from 1775 and the remaining four parts of volume I were issued between 1775 and 1778. The five parts of volume II were prepared in 1777 and issued in 1779 – though some plates had previously been issued singly in the 1760s. Volume III is a posthumous publication that lacks coherence of illustration or text.

There have been five reprints of the brothers' *Works* published this century: a facsimile edition by Thezard in Paris in 1902; reduced editions by Alec Tiranti, London, in 1939 and 1959 with an introductory essay by John Swarbrick; a further reduced edition of 1975 by Academy Editions, London, with an introduction by Robert Oresko; and a larger scale reduced edition by Dover Publications, Inc. with an introduction by Henry Hope Reed, New York, 1980.

Modern Studies on the Adam Brothers

John Swarbrick, *Robert Adam and his Brothers: their Lives, Work and Influence on English Architecture*, 1915.

Arthur T. Bolton, *The Architecture of Robert and James Adam 1758–1794*, 2 volumes, 1922.

This is the standard reference work on the brothers' practice compiled by the then curator of Sir John Soane's Museum and publishing the index to the collection of Adam drawings in the Soane Museum, prepared by Walter L. Spiers. Spiers's index has been reprinted separately as a companion to the microfilm edition of the Soane Museum Adam drawings published by Chadwick-Healey Ltd in 1979. The index lists in abbreviated form the contents of the 55 volumes of drawings and is available as a book, Walter L. Spiers, *Catalogue of the Drawings and Designs of Robert and James Adam in Sir John Soane's Museum*. It is unillustrated. Bolton's work was reprinted in 1985.

James Lees-Milne, *The Age of Adam*, 1947.

A general study of the Adams' architecture and that of their contemporaries.

John Fleming, *Robert Adam and his circle in Edinburgh and Rome*, 1962.

A fundamental study for an account of the brothers' background in Scotland, their early careers and for the genesis of the Adam style in Italy.

Iain G. Brown, '"The resemblance of a great genius", Commemorative portraits of Robert Adam', *The Burlington Magazine*, CXX (1978), pp. 444–461.

Geoffrey Beard, *The Work of Robert Adam*, 1978.

A useful short resumé of the architect's life and work published to mark the 250th anniversary of Adam's birth, with an excellent range of over 240 illustrations, a list of works, chronology and detailed bibliography.

Alistair Rowan, *Designs for Castles and Country Villas by Robert & James Adam*, 1985.

A reconstruction of a lost volume which the Adams intended to publish on their later architecture but which was left incomplete on their deaths.

Ann and Joseph Rykwert, *The Brothers Adam, The Men and the Style*, 1985.

A popular account, well illustrated though marred by numerous inaccuracies.

Adam Decoration and Ornament

Damie Stillman, *The Decorative Work of Robert Adam*, 1966.
Martha Blythe Gerson, 'A Glossary of Robert Adam's Neo-Classical Ornament', *Architectural History*, 24 (1981), pp. 59–82.

Adam Drawings

Arthur T. Bolton, 'The Classical and Romantic Compositions of Robert Adam', *Architectural Review*, 57 (1925), pp. 28 & 29.
Paul Oppé, 'Robert Adam's Picturesque Compositions', *Burlington Magazine*, 80 (1942), pp. 56–59.
Alan A. Tait, 'The Picturesque Drawings of Robert Adam', *Master Drawings*, 9 (1971), pp. 161–171.
Scottish Arts Council, *Robert Adam and Scotland The Picturesque Drawings*, Exhibition Catalogue by Alan A. Tait, 1972.
Scottish Record Office, *Robert Adam at Home 1728–1978 Drawings in the Collection of Blair Adam*, Exhibition Catalogue by Alan A. Tait, 1978.

Adam Furniture

Eileen Harris, *The Furniture of Robert Adam*, 1963.
Maurice Tomlin, *Catalogue of Adam Period Furniture*, Victoria and Albert Museum, 1972, second edition 1982.

Adam Silver

Robert Rowe, *Adam Silver*, 1965.

Short Historical Notices on Adam

The Gentleman's Magazine, 1792 (i), pp. 282–3 contains the obituary notice following Robert Adam's death. Both *The Dictionary of Architecture* edited by Wyatt Papworth for the Architectural Publications Society (1852–92) and *The Dictionary of National Biography*, edited by Leslie Stephens and Sidney Lee (1885–1922) contain historical entries on Robert Adam. Sir Lewis Namier and John Brooke, *The House of Commons 1754–1790*, II, 1964 pp. 7–8 gives an account of his career as a member of Parliament. The most detailed and scholarly brief account of the brothers' careers is provided by H. M. Colvin, in his *Biographical Dictionary of British Architects 1600–1840*, 1978, while Dr David King of the University of Stirling has compiled (1988) a complete descriptive catalogue of the brothers' executed work and its subsequent fate.

Bibliography of Works cited in the Catalogue

Adam 1773	Adam, R. & J. *The Works in Architecture of Robert and James Adam*, 3 vols., 1773 (vol. I), 1779 (vol. II), 1822 (vol. III).
Bolton 1922	Bolton, A. T. *The Architecture of Robert and James Adam 1758 - 1794*, 1922, 2 vols.
Colvin 1978	Colvin, H. *A Biographical Dictionary of English Architect*, 1978.
Edinburgh 1972	Scottish Arts Council, Edinburgh. *Robert Adam and Scotland: the Picturesque Drawings*, exhibition, 1972. Catalogue by A. A. Tait.
Edinburgh 1978	Scottish Record Office, Edinburgh. *Robert Adam at Home: Drawings from the Collection of Blair Adam*, exhibition, 1978. Catalogue by A. A. Tait.
Fensom 1984	Fensom, D. 'Geometric Form in Adam Architecture?', *Canadian Art Review* (December 1984), pp. 97–109.
Fleming 1958	Fleming, J. 'The Journey to Spalatro', *The Architectural Review*, No. 123 (1958), pp. 103–07.
Fleming 1962	Fleming, J. *Robert Adam and his circle in Edinburgh and Rome*, 1962.
Fleming 1968 I	Fleming, J. 'A "Retrospective View" by John Clerk of Eldin, with some comments on Adam's Castle Style', *Concerning Architecture: Essays Presented to Nikolaus Pevsner*, 1968, pp. 75–84.
Fleming 1968 II	Fleming, J. 'Robert Adam's Castle Style', *Country Life*, CXLIII, (1968), pp. 1356–1359, 1443–1447.
Fleming & Honour 1968	Fleming, J. Honour, H. 'Francis Harwood' *Festschrift Ulrich Middeldorf*, Berlin, 1968, pp. 510–16.
Friedman 1987	Friedman, J. 'Spencer House', *Apollo*, CXXVI (1987), pp. 81–99.
Hall 1982	Hall, I. 'Antiquity and Fashion: William Constable and Burton Constable', *Country Life*, CLXXI (1982), pp. 1358–1361.
Harris 1963	Harris, E. *The Furniture of Robert Adam*, 1963.
Harris 1970	Harris, J. *Sir William Chambers*, 1970.
Harris 1971	Harris, J. *Catalogue of the Drawings Collection of the Royal Institute of British Architects. Inigo Jones and John Webb*, Farnborough, 1971.
Harris 1987	Harris, L. *Robert Adam and Kedleston: The Making of a Neo-Classical Masterpiece*, 1987.
Hunt 1971	Hunt, J. 'Gosford House, East Lothian', *Country Life*, CL (1971), pp. 1048–1050.
Macaulay 1975	Macaulay, J. *The Gothic Revival 1745–1845*, 1975, Chap VI.
McWilliam 1978	McWilliam, C. *The Buildings of Scotland: Lothian*, Harmondsworth, 1978.
Mauchline 1974	Mauchline, M. *Harewood House*, Newton Abbot, 1974.
Parker 1963	Parker, J. 'The Caryatid Chimney piece from Chesterfield House', *The Metropolitan Museum of Art Bulletin*, Feb. 1963, pp. 202–213.
Spiers index	Spiers, W. L. *Topographical Index to the Collection of Adam Drawings*, Appendix to Bolton 1922, vol. 2.
Stillman 1966	Stillman, D. *The Decorative Work of Robert Adam*, 1966.
Stillman 1977	Stillman, D. 'Chimney-Pieces for the English Market: A Thriving Business in Late Eighteenth-Century Rome', *The Art Bulletin*, LIX, I (1977), pp. 85–94.
Stroud 1966	Stroud, D. *Henry Holland, His Life and Architecture*, 1966.
Robertson 1948	Robertson, M. 'The Golden Section or Golden Cut', *RIBA Journal*, LV (1948), pp. 536–543.

Rowan 1974 I — Rowan, A. 'The Adam Castle Style', *Journal of the Royal Society of Arts*, CXXII (1974), pp. 679–694.

Rowan 1974 II — Rowan, A. 'William Adam & Co.', *Journal of the Royal Society of Arts*, CXXII (1974), pp. 659–669.

Rowan 1974 III — Rowan, A. 'Wedderburn Castle, Berwickshire', *Country Life*, CLVI (1974), p. 356.

Rowan 1985 — Rowan, A. *Designs for Castles and Country Villas by Robert and James Adam*, London & New York, 1985.

Rowe 1967 — Rowe, R. *Adam Silver*, 1967.

Tait 1978 — Tait, A. A. 'The Sale of Robert Adam's Drawings', *The Burlington Magazine*, CXX (1978), pp. 451–454.

Tait 1981 — Tait, A. A. 'Robert Adam's Picturesque Architecture', *The Burlington Magazine*, CXXIII (1981), pp. 421–22.

V & A 1927 — Victoria and Albert Museum. *Catalogue of Watercolour Paintings*, 1927.

V & A 1984 — Victoria and Albert Museum. *Rococo, Art and Design in Hogarth's England*, exhibition, 1984.

Williams 1952 — Williams, I. *Early English Watercolours*, 1952.

Concordance of numbers

Museum No.	Cat. No.
80	190
86	110
2828	112
3324	55
3325	68
3326	58
3327	69
3328	145
3329	146
3330	147
3331	148
3332	60
3333	59
3334	74
3335	72
3436.4	56
3436.5	57
3436.6	3
3436.7	2
3436.8	11
3436.9	18
3436.10	14
3436.11	42
3436.12	144
3436.13	43
3436.14	73
3436.15	21
3436.16 (*recto*)	20
3436.16 (*verso*)	19
3436.17	16
3436.18 (*recto*)	6
3436.18 (*verso*)	15
3436.19	22
3436.20	28
3436.21	143
3436.22	29
3436.23 (*recto*)	37
3436.23 (*verso*)	161
3436.24	31
3436.25	38
3436.26	51
3436.27	39
3436.30	46
3436.31	48
3436.32	47
3436.33	45
3436.34	44
3436.35	30
3436.36	159
3436.37	40
3436.38	41
3436.39	35
3436.40	33
3436.41	101
3436.42	32
3436.43	34

Museum No.	Cat. No.
3436.44	36
3436.46	154
3436.47 (*recto*)	155
3436.47 (*verso*)	13
3436.48	193
3436.49	61
3436.50	17
3436.52	23
3436.53	10
3436.54	9
3436.55	162
3436.56	160
3436.59	8
3436.60	7
3436.61	149
3436.62	50
3436.63	49
3436.64	1
3436.234	5
3436.335	157
8158.4	196
8168	195
8897.14	156
9110.A	52
9110.B	12
19541.4	70
19541.5	71
334–1872	27
362–1885	4
D. 357–1885	194
D. 1839–1885	153
D. 1894–1889	25
130–1890	26
D. 299–1890	182
D. 300–1890	180
D. 301–1890	184
D. 302–1890	191
D. 303–1890	178
D. 304–1890	169
D. 305–1890	166
D. 306–1890	174
D. 307–1890	183
D. 308–1890	167
D. 309–1890	168
D. 310–1890	170
D. 311–1890	179
D. 312–1890	181
D. 313–1890	177
D. 314–1890	192
D. 315–1890	173
D. 316–1890	175
D. 317–1890	172
D. 318–1890	176
D. 319–1890	171
D. 275–1894	187

Museum No.	Cat. No.
D. 276–1894	188
D. 277–1894	185
D. 278–1894	186
D. 2165–1896	125
D. 2166–1896	114
D. 2167–1896	115
D. 2168–1896	116
D. 2169–1896	113
D. 2170–1896	131
D. 2171–1896	132
D. 2172–1896	134
D. 2173–1896	135
D. 2174–1896	136
D. 2175–1896	137
D. 2176–1896	133
D. 2177–1896	126
D. 2178–1896	117
D. 2179–1896	118
D. 2180–1896	119
D. 2181–1896	127
D. 2182–1896	128
D. 2183–1896	130
D. 2184–1896	120
D. 2185–1896	121
D. 2186–1896	122
D. 2187–1896	129
D. 2188–1896	142
D. 2189–1896	139
D. 2190–1896	140
D. 2191–1896	141
D. 2192–1896	138
D. 2193–1896	123
D. 2194–1896	124
D. 1251–1898	150
D. 1252–1898	151
D. 1253–1898	152
E. 2115–1913	158
E. 602–1918	163
E. 603–1918	164
E. 1–1937	53
E. 2–1937	54
P. 3–1938	24
E. 3225–1938	197
E. 1063–1940	111
OPH 396–1949	89
OPH 397–1949	88
OPH 398–1949	91
OPH 399–1949	85
OPH 400–1949	92
OPH 401–1949	108
OPH 402–1949	107
OPH 403–1949	105
OPH 404–1949	99
OPH 405–1949	87

Museum No.	Cat. No.
OPH 406–1949	94
OPH 407–1949	98
OPH 408–1949	90
OPH 409–1949	103
OPH 410–1949	79
OPH 411–1949	77
OPH 412–1949	81
OPH 413–1949	80
OPH 414–1949	78
OPH 415–1949	95
OPH 416–1949	96
OPH 417–1949	86
OPH 418–1949	97
OPH 419–1949	84
OPH 420–1949	93
OPH 421–1949	102
OPH 422–1949	82
OPH 423–1949	63
OPH 424–1949	66
OPH 425–1949	65
OPH 426–1949	64
OPH 427–1949	100
OPH 428–1948	83
OPH 428–1949	104
OPH 428B–1949	106
OPH 428C–1949	67
OPH 428D–1949	109
OPH 428E–1949	76
E. 967–1965	165
E. 968–1965	189
E. 973–1965	75

Index of names and places

Bold figures refer to main catalogue entries

Abrahams, Aleck, provenance of designs, *notes to* 163–164

Acland, Sir Thomas, Bt, *note to* 142

Adam, James, pp.11, 13–20, 24–25, 27; drawings by, 1 (pl.1)?, 24?, 27?; *notes to* 23, 27, 58,142

Adam, John, pp.11–14; *note to* 154

Adam, Robert, pp.11–27; drawings by and probably by, 1 (pl.1)?, 2 (pl.2), 3 (pl.3)?, 5?, 6 (pl.3), 7 (pl.4), 8 (pl.5), 9 (pl.6), 10–13, 15 (pl.9), 16, 17 (pl.10), 18?, 19?, 20, 24, 25 (pl.11), 26 (pl.12), 28 (pl.13), 29, 30 (pl.15), 31 (pl.16), 32–34, 35 (pl.17), 36–41, 52 (pl.20), 53 (pl.21), 54, 55 (pl.22), 56–57, 58 (pl.23), 59–60, 61 (pl.24), 63, 64 (pl.25), 65–66, 68 (pl.26), 69 (pls.27–28), 70, 71 (pl.29), 72 (pl.30), 73, 74 (pl.31), 76 (pl.32), 77 (pl.33), 78–79, 80 (pl.34), 81 (pl.35), 82–83, 84 (pl.38), 85 (pl.39), 86, 87 (pl.40), 88 (pl.41), 89 (pl.42), 90, 91 (pl.43), 92–93, 94 (pl.44), 95 (pl.45), 96 (pl.46), 97 (pls.47–48), 98–100, 101 (pl.49), 102 (pl.50), 103 (pl.51), 104–105, 106 (pl.52), 107 (pl.53), 108 (pl.54), 110 (pl.55), 111 (pl.56), 112–116, 117 (pl.57), 118–127, 128 (pl.58), 129, 130 (pl.65), 131, 132 (pl.59), 133 (pl.60), 134 (pl.61), 135 (pl.62), 136 (pl.63), 137 (pl.64), 143 (pl.67), 144 (pl.68), 145, 146 (pl.69), 147–149, 154 (pl.71), 155, 156 (pl.73), 157–162, 193; *notes to* 4, 14, 21–23, 42–44, 49–51, 62, 75,109, 142, 163, 181, 184, 188, 191–192, 194–195, 197: *see also* frontis.

Adam Street, *see* London: Westminster, City of

Adam, William, pp.11–14; *note to* 74

Adelphi Terrace, no.5, *see* London: Westminster, City of

Adelphi, the *see* London: Westminster, City of

Admiralty Screen, Whitehall, *see* London: Westminster, City of

Aesculapius, Temple of, *see* Split

Albemarle Street, no.13, *see* London: Westminster, City of

Algardi, Alessandro, *note to* 4

Alnwick, Northumberland, *note to* 144

Anonymous hands, drawings by, pp.11, 24; 4, 21–22, 42 (pl.18), 43 (pl.19), 44–51, 62, 67, 75, 109, 150–153, 163–177, 178 (pl.75), 179–190, 194 (pl.76), 195 (pl.77), 196–197; *note to* 154–192.

Apsley, Lord (later 2nd Earl Bathurst), *note to* 69

Apsley House, Hyde Park, *see* London: Westminster, City of

Argyll, 3rd Duke of, pp.11–12

Auchercruive, Ayrshire, *note to* 108

Audley End House, Essex, p.17

Bacon, John, *note to* 156

Bailey, George, pp.22, 25

Balbardie House, Bathgate, Lothian, *note to* 9

Barry, Sir Charles, *note to* 59

Bartolozzi, Francesco, engraving by, 14 (pl.8)

Bath, Avon: Pultney Bridge, *note to* 28

Bective, Ist Earl of, *note to* 35

Berkeley Square, Earl of Bute's house in, *see* London: Westminster, City of

Bernini, Gian Lorenzo, *note to* 5

Blair Adam, near Kinross, Tayside (the Adam family estate), pp.11, 14

Blair Drummond, Perthshire, *note to* 108

Bolton, 5th Duke of, *note to* 31

Bolton, A.T. p.24; *note to* 74

Boscawen, Admiral Edward, *note to* 154

Bowood House, Wiltshire, pp.13, 20; **52** (pl.20); *notes to* 29, 74

Brettingham, Matthew, pp.12–13

Bruges, J.P. de, p.14

Brunias, Agostino, p.25; *note to* 14

Buckingham House, Pall Mall, *see* London: Westminster, City of

Burlington, Richard Boyle, 3rd Earl of, *notes to* 54, 89

Burton Constable, Humberside (formerly East Yorkshire), *note to* 156

Bute, John Stuart, 3rd Earl of, p.12

Byron, Lord, *note to* 43

Calton Hill burying ground, *see* Edinburgh

Carr (of York), John, p.13; *note to* 59

Carter, John, *note to* 193

Casa Guarnieri, *see* Rome

Castle Semple, Strathclyde, *note to* 108

Cawthorn, James Fenton, MP, pp.22–23; *notes to* 145–147

Chambers, Sir William, pp.12, 15, 26; *notes to* 23, 80, 109, 181

Charlotte, Queen, *note to* 43

Chesterfield, 4th Earl of, *note to* 154

Chesterfield House, *see* London: Westminster, City of

Child, Francis, p.17; *notes to* 76–77, 80, 109

Child, Sir Francis (uncle of Francis and Robert Child) *notes to* 80–81

Child, Robert, pp.13, 16–19, 21; *notes to* 63–67, 75, 80–81, 84–86, 88–89, 91–92, 97, 102–103, 105, 107–108

Child, Samuel, *note to* 80

Christie, Manson and Wood, provenance of drawing, 111 (pl.56)

Cipriani, Giambattista, p.26; drawing partly by, 154 (pl.71)

Claude (Lorrain), *note to* 26

Clérisseau, Jacques-Louis, pp.12–13, 15; drawing by, 14 (pl.7); *notes to* 6, 8, 61, 108

Clerk, Susan, p.22

Clifford, 4th Lord, *note to* 130

Compton Verney, Warwickshire, pp.17, 19–20, 22; **53** (pl.21), **54**; *note to* 130

Cortona, Pietro da, *note to* 5

Cousins, *see* Cozens

Coventry, 6th Earl of, pp.22–23; *notes to* 55–56, 73

Cozens (Alexander or John Robert), p.26

Croome d'Abitot, Worcestershire:
  Church of St James the Apostle, p.19; **56–57**
  Croome Court, **55** (pl.22); *note to* 87

Crunden, John, p.22

Culzean Castle, Ayrshire, *notes to* 74, 108, 144, 148

Curzon, Sir Nathaniel, p.16

Dalkeith, Lothian, *note to* 74
Dalquharran Castle, Ayrshire, *notes to* 108, 144
Dalzell, Mr, *note to* 31
Daniell, William, RA, p.26
Davidson, Duncan, pp.16, 22–23; *note to* 144
Delaval, Sir John Hussey, Bt, *note to* 159
Deputy Ranger's Lodge Gateway, Green Park, *see* London: Westminster, City of
Derby, Earl of, *note to* 156
Derby House, Grosvenor Square, *see* London: Westminster, City of
Devall, John, p.20; *notes to* 70–71
Dewez, Laurent-Benôit, p.25; *note to* 14
Dillon, Lord, *note to* 70–71
Diocletian's Palace, *see* Split
Doria Pamphili, Villa, *see* Rome
Downing Street, *see* London: Westminster, City of
Drapers' Company, drawing lent by, 62
Drapers' Hall, Throgmorton Street, *see* London: City of
Drummond, John, *notes to* 191–192
Dundas, Sir Laurence, *note to* 73

Edinburgh, pp.11, 13, 15, 22:
  Calton Hill burying ground, *note to* 108
  University, p.11
Eglinton, 11th Earl of, *see* Montgomerie, the Hon. Archibald

Fitzroy Square, *see* London: Camden
Flaxman, John, p.26
Florence, Italy, *note to* 165
Fodrell, Gilbert, *note to* 75
Frederick, Sir Charles, *note to* 44

Gainsborough, Thomas, p.17
Gallilei Alessandro, *note to* 5
Gandy, Joseph Michael, p.26
Garrett, Robert, *note to* 147
Garrick, David, *notes to* 29, 74
Gawthorp House, *see* Harewood House
George III, pp.11–12, 15; *note to* 44
Gibbs, James, *note to* 54
Gillray, James, *note to* 42
Gilpin, the Rev William, p.17
Gordon, 4th Duke of, *note to* 68
Gordon, Lord William, pp.22–23; note to 68
Gorham, John, *note to* 62
Gosford House, East Lothian, p.21; **58** (pl.23)
Greenwich Palace, *see* London: Greenwich
Gresham, Sir Thomas, *note to* 80
Griffin, Sir John, Bt, *note to* 193
Gunnis, Rupert, provenance of design or drawing, 75, 165, 189

Hadrian's Villa, *see* Tivoli
Hamilton, David, *note to* 58
Hampton, Middlesex: David Garrick's villa at, *note to* 74
Hanover Square: house of Sir John Hussey Delaval, Bt, *see* London: Westminster, City of
Harborough, 4th Earl of, *note to* 31
Harewood House, Yorkshire, p.13; **59**, **69**; *notes to* 148, 154; *see also* pl.72
Harwood, Francis, *note to* 165
Hatchlands, Surrey, *notes to* 54, 154
Headfort House, Kells, Co. Meath, *note to* 35
Hendon Manor, *see* London: Barnet
Heston, Church of St Leonard, *see* London: Hounslow
Heywood Hill, G., provenance of drawing, *note to* 197
Hildburgh, Dr W.L., provenance of design or drawing, 53–54
Hobcraft, John, *note to* 137
Holland, 1st Lord, pp.18, 20–21; *note to* 72
Holland, Henry, p.24; designs by, 191–192; *note to* 154–192
Home House, 20 Portman Square, *see* London: Westminster, City of
Hope, the Hon. Charles, p.12
Hopetoun, 1st Earl of, p.11
Hopetoun, 2nd Earl of, p.12; *notes to* 44, 154
Hopetoun House, Lothian, p.11
Hume, David, *note to* 108
Hyde Park Corner, Triumphal Gateway, *see* London: Westminster, City of

Inveraray Castle, Strathclyde, p.11

Jackson, R., provenance of design or drawing, 12, 25, 52, 195
John Adam Street, *see* London: Westminster, City of
Johnson, John, designs and drawings by, 138–142
Jones, Inigo, *notes to* 10, 73, 89
Juvarra, Filippo, *note to* 5

Kames, Lord Henry Home, *note to* 73
Kedleston Hall, Derbyshire, pp.12, 16; **61** (pl.24); *note to* 8
Kent, William, pp.15, 17, 26; *note to* 7
Kenwood House, Hampstead, *see* London: Camden
Kew Gardens, *see* London: Richmond
Killerton Park, near Exeter, Devon, *note to* 142
Kinnoull, 8th Earl of, p.17
Kirkcaldy, Fife, p.11

Lacey, S., engraving by, 130 (pl.66)
Langley, Batty, *note to* 74
Lanser, G., provenance of design or drawing, 185–188
Lascelles, Edwin, *notes to* 59–60
Le Roy, J.D., *note to* 72
Leith, Lothian, p.11; *see also* Merchiston (North)
Liardet, M., p.14
Lisbon, Portugal: design for a royal palace, **6** (pl.3)
Lisburne, 1st Earl of, p.19; *notes to* 113–114, 117, 120–121, 130, 142
Lloyds offices, *see* London: City of
LONDON:
  Barnet (formerly Middlesex):
    Hendon Manor, **74** (pl.31); *note to* 29
  Camden:
    Fitzroy Square, p.14
    Kenwood House, Hampstead, p.13

Lincoln's Inn Fields: no. 13 (Sir John Soane's Museum), pp.11, 16–18, 22–23, 25–27; drawing from, 97 (pl.48); *notes to* 6, 9, 52, 55, 58, 68–72, 74, 77, 79–80, 87, 89–90, 92, 97, 101–102, 107, 112, 130, 137, 143, 154, 157, 159, 193
City of:
Drapers' Hall, Throgmorton Street, p.19; **62**
Lloyds offices, *note to* 52
Greenwich:
Greenwich Palace, *note to* 73
Hounslow (formerly Middlesex):
Church of St Leonard, Heston, **75**
Osterley Park, pp.13, 16–22; **76** (pl.32), **77** (pl.33), **78–79**, **80** (pl.34), **81** (pl.35), **82–83**, **84** (pl.38), **85–86**, **87** (pl.40), **88** (pl.41), **89** (pl.42), **90**, **91** (pl.43), **92–93**, **94** (pl.44), **95** (pl.45), **96** (pl.46), **97** (pls.47–48), **98–100**, **101** (pl.49), **102** (pl.50), **103** (pl.51), **104–105**, **106** (pl.52), **107** (pl.53), **108** (pl.54), **109**; *notes to* 15, 35, 75, 75, 137, 148; *see also* pl.36 (photograph of) (pl.37) (plan as completed 1763–82); provenance of design or drawing, 63–67, 76–100, 102–109
Syon House, Isleworth, pp.13, 16, 19–21, 24; **110** (pl.55), **111** (pl.56); *notes to* 10, 50, 69, 92
Lambeth:
Vauxhall Gardens, *note to* 74
Richmond (formerly Surrey):
Duke of Montagu's House, p.19; **112**
Kew Gardens, *note to* 23
Westminster, City of
Adam Street, p.14
Adelphi, the, pp.13–14, 24; *note to* 59
Adelphi Terrace, no.5 (David Garrick's house), *note to* 74
Admiralty Screen, Whitehall, pp.13–17
Albemarle Street, no. 13 (the Adam office), p.14
Apsley House, Hyde Park Corner, *notes to* 69, 197
Berkeley Square, no. 38 (Robert Child's house), **63–67**
Buckingham House, Pall Mall, *note to* 44
Chesterfield House, South Audley Street, *note to* 154
Deputy Ranger's Lodge Gateway, Green Park, p.24; **68** (pl.26)
Derby House, no. 23 (later 26) Grosvenor Square, *note to* 156
Downing Street, *note to* 192
Hanover Square: house of Sir John Hussey Delaval, Bt, *note to* 159
Home House, no. 20 Portman Square p.16; *note to* 148
Hyde Park Corner, Triumphal Gateway, pp.21, 23; **69** (pls.27–28); *note to* 10
John Adam Street, p.14
Lansdowne House, Berkeley Square (Earl of Bute's house), p.12
Lower Grosvenor Street (the Adam office), pp.13, 16
Mansfield Street: house for the Dowager Countess of Warwick, *note to* 70–71
Mansfield Street, no. 13 (house built by John Devall), **70**, **71** (pl.29)
Oriental Club, Stratford Place, *note to* 156; *see also* pl.74 (photograph of library chimneypiece)
Piccadilly, no. 106 (formerly 29), **73**
Piccadilly House, Piccadilly, p.21, 72, (pl.30)
Portland House, p.18
Portland Place, p.14; *note to* 70–71
Robert Street, p.14
St George's Hospital, Hyde Park, *note to* 69
Somerset House, Strand, p.23
Spencer House, Green Park, *note to* 73
Spring Gardens, no. 16 (John Drummond's house), *note to* 192
Lower Grosvenor Street (the Adam office), *see* London: Westminster, City of
Luton Hoo, Bedfordshire, p.12
Lutyens, Sir Edwin, *note to* 70–71

McPherson, James, *note to* 30
Mamhead House, Devon, pp.19, 21–22; **113–116**, **117** (pl.57), **118–127**, **128** (pl.58), **129**, **130–131**, **132** (pl.59), **133** (pl.60), **134** (pl.61), **135** (pl.62), **136** (pl.63), **137** (pl.64), **138–142**; *note to* 92; *see also* pl.65 (drawing from Sir John Soane's Museum), pl.66 (engraving by S. Lacey)
Mansfield, Lord Chief Justice, *note to* 142
Mansfield, 1st Earl of, p.13
Mansfield Street: house for the Dowager Countess of Warwick, *see* London: Westminster, City of
Mansfield Street, no. 13 (house built by John Devall), *see* London: Westminster, City of
Melbourne, 1st Lord, *note to* 72
Mellerstain, Berwickshire, *notes to* 87, 137
Merchiston (North), Leith: John Adam's Villa at, p.14
Michelangelo (Buonarroti), *notes to* 10, 69
Mistley Hall, Norfolk, p.16; **143** (pl.67); *note to* 102
Montagu, Duke of, pp.19, 22–23; *note to* 112
Montgomerie, the Hon. Archibald (later 11th Earl of Eglinton), *note to* 68
Moor Park, Hertfordshire, p.17; *note to* 73

Nash, John, p.26
National Monuments Record, photograph from, pl.36
National Monuments Record for Scotland, *note to* 58
Neale, J.P., 130; engraving after, pl.66
Newby Hall, Yorkshire, p.16
Newman, Sir Ralph, Bt, *note to* 137
Newstead Abbey, Nottinghamshire, *note to* 43
Niger, Caius Pescennius, *note to* 22
Nollekens, Joseph, RA, *note to* 154
Northumberland, Earl of (later 1st Duke of), p.13; *note to* 110
Nostell Priory, Yorkshire, *notes to* 87, 137, 148

Oriental Club, Stratford Place, *see* London: Westminster, City of
Osterley Park, *see* London: Hounslow

Pain, William, p.22
Paine, James, pp.12, 21–22; *note to* 43
Palatine, the, *see* Rome
Palladio, Andrea, *note to* 28
Palmyra, Syria: Temple of the Sun, *note to* 97
Pamfili, Prince Camillo, *note to* 4
Pannini, G.B., p.16
Pantheon, the, *see* Rome
Parke, Henry, p.26
Parsons, E., p.24; provenance of design or drawing, 70–71, 150–153, 156, 166–184, 191–192, 194, 196

Paterson, John, *note to* 58
Peacock, James, p.25
Pearson, J.L., *note to 70–71*
Piazza del Popolo, *see* Rome
Piazza di Spagna, *see* Rome
Piccadilly, no. 106 (formerly 29), *see* London: Westminster, City of
Piccadilly House, *see* London: Westminster, City of
Piranesi, Giovanni Battista, pp.12–13, 15; *notes to* 101, 156; *see also* frontis.
Pitfour Castle, Perthshire, *notes to* 108, 144
Portland, William Cavendish, 3rd Duke of, p.18
Portland House, *see* London: Westminster, City of
Portland Place, *see* London: Westminster, City of
Portman Square, no. 20, *see* London: Westminster, City of
Pulteney Bridge, *see* Bath

Quarenghi, Giacomo, *note to* 6

Raby Home Farm, Co. Durham, *note to* 43
Ravenna, Italy: Theodoric's mausoleum, *note to* 108
Richardson, Charles James, pp.22–27; provenance of design or drawing, 1–11, 13–23, 28–51, 55–61, 68–69, 72–74, 101, 112, 143–149, 154–155, 157, 159–162, 193
Richardson, George, p.19; *note to* 62
Rigby, Rt. Hon Richard, MP, *note to* 143
Rimell & Son, provenance of design or drawing, 113–137
Robert Street, *see* London: Westminster, City of
Robertson, Daniel, drawing by, 23
Rome, Italy, pp.12 15, 21; *notes to* 3, 6–8, 61:
  Casa Guarnieri, *note to* 13
  Doria Pamphili, Villa, **4**
  Palatine, the, *note to* 15
  Pantheon, the, p.16; *notes to* 19, 22
  Piazza del Popolo, *note to* 7
  Piazza di Spagna, *note to* 13
  Santa Trinità dei Monti, **13**; *note to* 155
Rowlandson, Thomas, *note to* 42
Rysbrack, John Michael, *note to* 154

St George's Hospital, Westminster, *see* London: Westminster, City of
St James the Apostle, *see* Croome d'Abitot
St Leonard, Heston, *see* London: Hounslow
Saltram House, Devon, *note to* 102
Salvin, Anthony, *note to* 130
Santa Trinità dei Monti, *see* Rome
Severus, Septimius, *note to* 22
Shardeloes House, near Amersham, Buckingham, *notes to* 54, 92
Shelburne, 2nd Earl of, p.13
Smith, Samuel, *note to* 31
Soane, Sir John, pp.22–23, 25–26
Soane Museum, *see* London: Camden
Somerset House, *see* London: Westminster, City of
Southill House, Bedfordshire, *note to* 192
Spalato (and Spalatro), *see* Split
Spencer, 1st Earl, *note to* 73
Spencer House, Green Park, *see* London: Westminster, City of
Spiers, Walter, pp.22, 25
Split, Yugoslavia:
  Diocletian's Palace, p.13; *note to* 72
  Aesculapius, Temple of, **14** (pls.7–8)
Spring Gardens, no. 14 (John Drummond's house), *see* London: Westminster, City of
Stothard, Thomas, RA, p.26
Stowe Park, Buckinghamshire, p.17; *note to* 9
Stuart, James, pp.21–22
Syon House, Isleworth, *see* London: Hounslow

Taylor, Sir Robert, *note to* 80
Theodoric's mausoleum, *see* Ravenna
Tivoli, Italy, *note to* 15: Hadrian's Villa, p.16; *note to* 61
Tulloch Castle, Cromarty, Highland Region, p.16; **144** (pl.68)
Tullysoul, *note to* 30

Ugbrooke Park, Devon, *note to* 130

Van Gelder, Peter Matthias, *note to* 75
Vanburgh, Sir John, p.26; *notes to* 10, 28
Vanvitelli, Luigi, p.16
Vardy, John, *note to* 73
Vauxhall Gardens, *see* London: Lambeth
Venice, Italy, *note to* 89
Versailles, France, *note to* 50
Vignola (Giacomo Barozzi da Vignola), *note to* 1
Vitruvius Pollio, M., *note to* 73

Wallington, Northumberland, *note to* 43
Walpole, Horace, p.25; *note to* 50
Ware, Isaac, *notes to* 54, 154
Warwick, Dowager Countess of, *notes to* 70–71
Webb, John, *note to* 73
Wemyss, 7th Earl of, pp.22–23; *notes to* 31, 58
Westmorland, Sarah, Countess of, *note to* 75
William Adam & Co, pp.13–14; *notes to* 23, 70–71
Willoughby de Broke, 6th Lord, *note to* 53
Wilson, Richard, p.17
Wilton, Joseph, *note to* 165
Woburn Abbey, Bedfordshire, *note to* 192
Wormleybury, Hertfordshire, *note to* 148
Wyatt, James, pp.13, 22, 26
Wynn, Sir Watkin Williams, *note to* 156
Wyreside, near Cockerham, Lancashire, pp.19, 22; **145**, **146** (pl.69), **147**; *see also* pl.70 (engraving of entrance front)

Zucchi, Antonio, *notes to* 87, 92